Windows and Mirrors

Short Stories   Volume 2

Editor: Marilyn Chapman

Prentice-Hall Canada Inc., Scarborough, Ontario

For Gayle and Doug, forever.

Canadian Cataloguing in Publication Data

Main entry under title:

Windows and mirrors: short stories

For use in high schools.
ISBN 0-13-960485-5 (v. 1) ISBN 0-13-960444-8 (v. 2)

1. Short stories, Canadian (English).*   2. Readers
(Secondary). I. Chapman, Marilyn, date

PE1121.W56 1987   C813'.01'08   C85-099286-9

Accompanying Materials

Windows and Mirrors: Short Stories Volumes 1 and 2 and Teacher's Guides

© 1987 by Prentice-Hall Canada Inc., Scarborough, Ontario

Prentice-Hall, Inc., Englewood Cliffs, New Jersey
Prentice-Hall International, Inc., London
Prentice-Hall of Australia, Pty., Ltd., Sydney
Prentice-Hall of India Pvt., Ltd., New Delhi
Prentice-Hall of Japan, Inc., Tokyo
Prentice-Hall of Southeast Asia (PTE) Ltd., Singapore
Editora Prentice-Hall do Brasil Ltda., Rio de Janeiro
Prentice-Hall Hispanoamericana, S.A., Mexico

1 2 3 4 5 6 D 92 91 90 89 88 87

Printed and bound in Canada by John Deyell Company

Project Editor: Paula Pettitt
Production Editor: Nicole Nathan
Production: Irene Maunder
Series Design: Brian Bean
Composition: CompuScreen Typesetting Ltd.
Cover: Coley's Point by Christopher Pratt, 1973, oil on board. Private Collection.
   Courtesy Mira Godard Gallery.

Contents

Stories are listed alphabetically by author's last name. At the back of the *Teacher's Guide*, stories are listed according to motifs and topics; terms and concepts; and thematic and stylistic complexity.

Preface

Windows and Mirrors is a two-volume anthology of Canadian short stories intended for secondary-school students across the country. The stories that appear in Volume 1 were selected to appeal to students with a wide range of abilities in grades nine and ten; the stories in Volume 2, to appeal to senior students with a wide range of abilities in grades eleven and twelve. It is not assumed that all of the stories in either volume will be suitable for any *one* class. Teachers may wish to consult the *Teacher's Guide*, where the stories are listed according to thematic and stylistic complexity, before making their selections.

All of the stories in Volume 2, and most of the stories in Volume 1, are written by authors who have produced at least one critically acclaimed volume of short stories. The main emphasis for the selection of stories in Volume 1 was on content appeal; the main emphasis for the selection of stories in Volume 2 was on literary excellence.

More than 1200 stories were read initially. From this number 110 were identified as "possibilities"; that is, their language and subject matter were appropriate for students at this level, their narratives were appealing, and the style in which they were written was representative of the author's work.

These "possibilities" were then narrowed down to 50 stories by applying the following criteria:

- Were most of Canada's well-known short-fiction writers represented, along with a few promising new writers?
- Were the stories teachable?
- Were a variety of genres, styles, and tones represented?
- Was there a reasonable representation of authors and protagonists of both sexes?
- Were all of Canada's main geographical regions represented by the authors?

The final selections were made by a group of eleven students. Their only criterion: were the stories "a good read"?

The stories are arranged alphabetically by the author's last name in the text. At the back of the *Teacher's Guide* stories are listed according to motifs and topics, terms and concepts, and thematic and stylistic complexity.

Among those authors represented in Volume 1 of this series are W.P. Kinsella, Farley Mowat, Alden Nowlan, Merna Summers, and Rudy Wiebe.

Marilyn Chapman

Acknowledgments

With special thanks to Gayle Baxter and Marie Gardner for their insights, suggestions, and good humour. Thanks also to Diane Hummel, the Department of English at Cameron Heights Collegiate (for assistance with the Glossary), and to student readers: Joy Barlow, Patrice Brown, Laura Dick, Michelle De Carlis, Carol DeVrieze, Chris Moser, Kelly Pineault, Shelley Rowe, Dave Spielmacher, Sonia Steeb, Wendy Veugen.

To David Steele, Paula Pettitt, Nicole Nathan, and Brian Bean of Prentice-Hall, my thanks for your encouragement and for the skill and dedication you used in turning the manuscript into the finished product.

To the Student

As adolescents move into adulthood, they begin to see that the world around them is not simple; rather, it is complex, unpredictable, and filled with unknowns. While young adults can do little to mitigate the complexity and unpredictability of this world, they can, if they choose, explore its unknowns. If they decide to do so, they will move beyond the narrow confines of their own experience and discover that knowledge is not merely a goal in itself, but is the means by which other goals can be achieved. The more people know about themselves, about others, and about the world around them, the more likely they are to find fulfillment in the future.

But how can one acquire this kind of knowledge? Where and when should one begin?

One acquires knowledge in many different ways: from experience, books, travel, conversations, and so on; all one needs is an inquiring mind. Equipped with such a mind, one begins here, now, today, and with whatever resources one has at hand—in this case, with a book of short stories.

How can one gain knowledge from stories? Are they not simply make-believe, or fictitious?

If stories are fictitious, they are so only in their outer dress— that is, in the names of the characters, and in the details of plot and setting. In their soul or essence, however, stories are true, for they teach us a great deal about other people, about ourselves, and about the world around us.

As the title of this anthology suggests, stories function as windows; windows that reveal not only the physical details of other people's lives, but their thoughts and feelings as well. Sometimes we learn more about these people than they know about themselves. In the process we put ourselves, however briefly, into someone else's shoes, thus moving beyond the confines of our own experience into a world we had not previously known.

But stories can function as mirrors as well as windows, mirrors that reflect truths about *ourselves* and the world in which we live. When we are reading these stories and feel a sudden tug of recognition, when we find ourselves thinking, "That's exactly what I would have done" or "That's exactly how I would have felt", then the stories are functioning as mirrors, revealing and clarifying some aspect of our own lives that we had not previously recognized.

However, like all great works of art, these stories not only reveal truth, they also delight, fascinate, and entertain.

So sit back and enjoy!

Under the I

Harold Sampson stamped his work boots on the coco mat two or three times, then scraped them backward like a dog after defecation, flinging snow against the doorsill behind him. This was his ritualistic winter entrance, a prairie habit he hadn't been able to leave behind when they sold the farm and moved to Calgary fourteen years ago.

There was a long white banner tacked on the bulletin board to his right. "BINGO," Harold read in large red letters, "THURSDAY, JANUARY 7, 8 P.M., SOUTHMOUNT LEGION HALL."

He hunched his shoulders and shook spasmodically. His large hands were clenched in fists, red from the cold, with white knuckles and fingernails. He stuck long arms straight out in front of him, like stovepipes extended to conduct the heat back into his body. He coughed loudly, too many times, for he smoked heavily these days. He drew the phlegm up to the front of his mouth between his teeth and spat on the floor to his right.

He had thick lips which were always

EDNA
ALFORD

somewhat wet with spittle on the inner edges; a common face, flat and wide and grey-bristled on the lower cheeks and chin. He had a round inoffensive nose and he was the sort of person who is always slightly brown, winter and summer. His grey eyes weren't small but looked that way because of the suggestion of a squint caused by the fine lines that grew like webs from the corners.

The spitting ceremony complete, Harold stuck his hands into his parka pockets and cocked his head, which was covered with one of those plaid wool caps with fleece ear flaps. He looked around the entrance of the hall for Mavis. She had run in from the cold while he parked the truck. Mavis wasn't there; probably in the ladies, he thought.

He waited, surveying the entrance hall. Wouldn't be too many out for the bingo tonight what with the blizzard blowing up so fast. He hadn't been taken with the idea of going out tonight but Mavis had insisted, saying that the bingo was pretty well all the fun she got out of life. So they had come.

He absently read the announcements on the bulletin board:

> Garage Sale. Sat. Jan. 9. 1322 42 Ave. S.W. Trike, crib, skates, doilies, and other household oddments. 10 a.m.-4 p.m.

> Funeral for Mrs. Bertha McNaughton, Sat. Jan. 9, 2:30 p.m. Legion Hall. Baking and sandwiches to be brought to Alice Thackeray 10 a.m. kitchen.

> Ladies Auxiliary Meeting Tues. Jan. 12. Legion Hall. Election of officers.

Again he looked to the top of the stairway for Mavis and this time she was there, beckoning him to come up. She wore her brown cloth coat with imitation leather trim on the collar, the cuffs, and in a narrow panel down the front. The plastic leather had cracked in the cold and was scarred with tiny fissures. The coat was shapeless. Her winter boots, imitation sealskin, looked strange, like paws on the ends of her short thick legs. She had pincurled her hair that morning and it stuck out mouse-brown, fluffy and festive. And she had put on lipstick. The fluffy hair and lipstick didn't soften her features as they might have but rather accentuated her sharp nose, tiny pig-like eyes, and thin mouth set low in a pointed chin. She never wore her hat after she had curled her hair, not even in this weather.

She looked sort of happy, Harold thought as he climbed the stairs slowly, for he had had a hard day at the plant, one of those long dark winter days where nothing had gone wrong exactly, but nothing had gone right either. The story of their lives. Nothing really terrible, but no breaks in the monotony. That was why Mavis liked the bingos, he figured, not so much for the chance to make a little extra money although, God knows, they could use it, but for the excitement.

Harold hated the bingos. Mostly women who were strangers to him yacking, smoking, drinking coffee and shrieking "BINGO" so loud you'd think they'd just jumped over the moon instead of winning $13.50 in quarters. But Mavis didn't drive so he had to come, especially tonight with the weather so bad; she couldn't depend on the buses.

When he got to the top of the stairs they went into the hall without speaking, Harold with his hands still stuck in his parka pockets. From an attendant, Mavis accepted a narrow white sheet of paper on which was listed the order of the bingos and what they were—"snowballs," "sandwiches," "postage stamps," "blackouts"—the list looked endless to Harold.

He had been wrong about the turnout. The Legion Hall was packed with people sorting their cards, getting coffee in white styrofoam cups from tall aluminum urns with black plastic spouts, establishing their separate territories like animals at the long plywood tables. They were mostly women, Harold was right about that, mostly middle-aged and older, with scarves, caps, and heavy stockings, hovering around their chairs which were wood and metal and could be stacked against the far wall after the bingo.

Mavis picked their seats and Harold followed her like a large friendly dog. She took off her coat, draped it over the back of her chair and said to Harold, "Take off your cap; you'll cook in here. How many cards you want?"

"Oh six, I guess. Might's well," Harold said. He swiped his cap off his head and dropped it on the floor beside him. His stubble-grey hair was flattened in a ring by the sweat band inside the cap.

Mavis went over to the table in the corner where the cards were stacked. There were a lot of people jostling around the table, snatching stacks of cards out from under each other, flipping through them rapidly, discarding the "bad ones" and grabbing more. They were searching diligently for the "right ones," the "good cards." Harold could never figure out how they could tell the good cards from the bad. Maybe that was his trouble, he thought. But he knew Mavis always took a great deal of care choosing the cards and although he did not himself know the ins and outs of the process, he had always trusted her judgment in these matters.

While she was gone, Harold looked around the hall. At first glance it looked large and open and well-lit but this first impression was deceptive. The walls were two-tone, painted pea green on the upper half and dirty sand on the lower half. These colours were divided by a narrow dark brown line which ran around the room, a sinister line like an elastic band you could expect to tighten imperceptibly or snap at any moment without warning.

Harold noticed there were almost as many fluorescent rods on the ceiling here as at Woolco, but fluorescent lighting never seemed to give enough light—he had noticed that wherever he went. No matter how many rods they put in, only the top half of the room seemed to be lit. And it was the same here. The bottom half, where the people were, was dingy somehow and he found himself squinting more than usual. The painters at the plant said fluorescent bulbs even changed the actual colour of a thing—you couldn't tell what the real colour was, they said, till you got it outside in the natural light.

He looked toward the stage where the caller would soon be seated. To the right of the bingo machine hung a picture of the Queen. To the left, a picture of Prince Philip. And in the centre, above the stage, an enormous Red Ensign had been tacked to the wall. Like most Legions, thought Harold. Most of them had the same kind of decoration. Some hung scrolls with names of the local war dead on them in that strange writing so an ordinary person couldn't read them.

By and by Mavis brought back fifteen cards, six for him and nine for her. She was pretty good at keeping track of them all so she always got nine instead of six, and tonight she had bought a Bonanza card, six cards full of numbers on one sheet to be played after the regular cards. She picked up a clean ashtray from one of the other tables and placed it between them. Harold reached into his shirt pocket and pulled out his package of Exports; he flicked one out by tapping the package expertly and lit the cigarette. Mavis smoked Matinees.

"They're just about ready to start, Harol'," said Mavis. She had never pronounced the "d" at the end of his name. "Why don't you run over and get us a coffee."

Harold got up and stood in line at one of the urns and got two cups of coffee, both with cream and sugar, both with little pink plastic stirsticks in them. As he was carrying them back to the table, the caller began reading the Legion announcements. They were the same ones Harold had already read, and he only half-heard the voice. He was concentrating on not spilling the coffees. "The funeral for Mrs. B. McNaughton," the voice said, "will be held in the Legion Hall Saturday, January 9 at 2:30 p.m. All you ladies are to bring your baking and sandwiches to the kitchen by 10 a.m. and give them to Mrs. Thackeray—," and so on.

By the time Harold returned to his seat, the caller had begun and Mavis glared at him for being late so that he jerked a little setting the coffees and slopped some onto two of Mavis' cards. Mavis stiffened and hissed at him to "Hurry up, Harol'." As he sat down, he sucked in his breath and sort of whistle-sighed it all out. For some reason this habit was of comfort to him when he was in Mavis' "bad books," although he knew full well that it irritated her even further.

The little white balls, housed in a small wire cage situated to the right of the caller, bounced frenetically. Each was marked with a number and the caller had only to place his hand over an orifice at the top of the cage and a numbered ball would pop into the palm of his hand. The number on that ball was what he called into the microphone, out to the crowd. And the Legion had just installed a new device for the bingos, a large electronic scoreboard which had been placed high above the caller's head and on which all the numbers called lit up.

This impressed Harold. He was always happy when they introduced a new machine at the plant. Kind of made some excitement in his day, he thought. Even so, the scoreboard rather frightened him, seeing his bad luck in lights. The thought never occurred to Harold that he might win. He never had. It was the same at the plant. He never thought about being promoted. Always someone else had been chosen. He was used to it.

"Under the O clickety-click sixty-six, O sixty-six," the caller said. His voice was strong and clear, slightly nasal, but confident, like the rest of the world, it seemed to Harold, like he was the caller for the whole world.

The balls spewed relentlessly and the caller called them arbitrarily and without passion. Number after number until finally a woman's voice cried out "Bingo!" The voice seemed detached from any person, like what Harold had heard about in the church, "speaking in tongues," he thought they called it, or was it "with tongues"? It didn't matter, he thought; it was all the same anyway. He looked down at his own cards while the caller checked the first bingo. There were a few spaces blacked out by the plastic slots with tabs on the cards, but no orderly row, no cause for excitement.

Harold butted his cigarette in the ashtray and absently flicked all the tabs back so the numbers showed again. Mavis did the same, only she was very businesslike about it, efficient, in fact. For her the process was like a job, to be accomplished with skill. For some reason it didn't represent loss to her, or the reiteration of loss as it did to Harold.

The next set of bingos was what they called a "postage stamp combination." "You better keep your mind on the cards this time if you know what's good for you, Harol'," Mavis said. Harold didn't look up at her, but stared at the patchwork of numbers on his bottom left card.

While everyone prepared for this game, a woman spoke to Harold from across the table. Harold hadn't noticed her before. She must have come in when he was off fetching the coffees. She was an old woman, about seventy-five or eighty he guessed, and she was all gussied up but in a poor way. That is she wore a lot of lipstick and an old but brightly coloured silk scarf pinned at the throat with a rhinestone brooch. The brooch had some of the strategic stones missing so you couldn't really tell what the pattern was supposed to represent. A bit like a bird, thought Harold. Yes, it was probably a bird. She had snow white hair, curly, that stuck out from under an absurd pink felt hat which nestled in a cloud of chartreuse net and pink feathers. Maybe that was why he thought of the bird.

She had remarkable eyes, hollow grey eyes that had no sparkle, no light in them. But that's the kind of thing age does to some, he thought, makes them spooky. What the woman said to him, however, was not remarkable. "I never miss a bingo," she said.

"Oh, s'at so," said Harold.

"Never in twenty-five years have I missed one week of the bingos. Before we came to the city, I used to play in Sundre, at the hall there. Better days, those were. I knew everybody in the hall. Here, I come alone and I go alone. And there was none of this fancy stuff then. Plain bingo. You have to be a mathematician these days jest to play."

"Oh," said Harold. He was not honestly interested but he had a way about him he couldn't seem to change. He listened to everybody no matter how boring, how tedious, how insignificant the conversation seemed to him. He was always tangled up with one lonely person or another, listening, not knowing how to stop listening to their stories. Mavis really hated this. She was always the one who had to drag him away.

Mavis, in fact, now put her finger to her lips and made a shushing sound. The caller had started again. "Under the B, the wee one, B one," he said, "B one." The voice became hypnotic after a while and table after table of human robots obeyed his every command, sliding the slots shut over their numbers. "More and more, under the N forty-four, N number forty-four."

Finally, after all the postage stamps had been filled and someone yelled "Bingo!", there was a break in the action. The lady across the table began to talk to Harold. He tried to appear busy sliding the slots back but it was useless and eventually he looked up at her and listened.

"I liked the old way," she said, "when we used the corn kernels or the pennies to cover the numbers. Can't get used to these silly slidin' cards, you know. Oh well," and this next part interested Harold, "I never win anyway," she said, "so what's the difference?" She smiled.

And Harold smiled showing his crooked teeth, ochre with nicotine. "Same with me," he said, "been comin' for years and I never won a cent."

"The cards are good, Harol'" interrupted Mavis. "I picked them as best I could. Maybe if you paid more attention."

"I don't see you winning nothin' tonight Mavis," he said, and as soon as he said it he knew he had gone too far. Mavis appeared to stop breathing for an instant as if he'd slapped her face. Then she grew cold and sat silent, her small eyes as glazed as a dead woman's. She stayed that way, waiting for the caller. Harold thought he shouldn't have done it, spoiled her night out is what she would say and maybe it was so, but nothing short of winning could turn it back—he knew that. She wouldn't be talking again till they got in the truck to go home, and then he would hear about it.

The old woman understood. He could see that by the way she looked at him and then at Mavis. He was getting to like her, warming up to her as they put it.

"So you never won in all them years," he said, half smiling, hoping she would accept this as an apology for his harsh behavior.

"Not once," she replied. "But this is my night. I'm going to win the big one tonight."

Harold laughed. "That's what they all say," he snorted, but he was sorry he had said that too. Her face was deadly serious.

"I'm not joking, young man," she said and Harold liked that. It had been a very long time since anyone had called him "young man." The old woman shifted her weight forward so that she was leaning toward him and she whispered conspiratorially. "Tonight, I know. I know I'm going to hit the jackpot tonight."

"If you say so," said Harold. He crossed his legs defensively, picked up his Exports and tapped one out. Before he lit it, he gulped down some of his sweet lukewarm coffee. He felt uneasy. Not that he wanted to disappoint the old girl. But he began to think she was a bit off, a little touched. Meeting someone like that always scared him.

The caller began again. A short one, he said, a "snowball," he called it. "Under the O, the old age pension number sixty-five. Ladies and gentlemen, O sixty-five."

"That one's for you," Harold said to the old woman.

"You bet'cher life," she laughed back at him as she carefully pushed a slot shut on one of the cards. She only played two cards. "Gettin' old," she told him, "though I never played more than two. Never could manage to keep track of more."

"You're not the only one," Harold said, feeling more and more of an affinity to this strange old woman.

No more than a dozen or so numbers had been called when someone yelled "Bingo" and the snowball was over. The caller marched verbally through the letters "L" and "X" and the "sandwiches," calmly articulating number after number, event after event, according to the program. Finally he took a break, said he'd be back in ten minutes and that then they would go for the "total blackout" and the winner would take the jackpot which tonight was $377.50.

The old woman smiled to herself, then looked up at Harold. "Don't worry about me," she said, "I mean the not winning. It's never been any different for me. I had two boys and one of them died, the good one. They say it's always so. You put me in mind of him somehow. The other, I don't know where he got to. He was a drunk and no good for nothin', even on the farm.

"We never had a thing. My man was no farmer neither. If it wasn't for my cream and egg money, we'd a starved. If there was hail around, it always hit us and if there were hoppers, we had the worst of 'em. Not one bit different when we left the farm. Hand to mouth all them years. I'm glad I'm done with it."

Here he was again, listening. Good old Harold. But it was somehow different this time. All of it sounded so familiar. Everything rang a bell, as they say, until Harold was fairly ringing all over inside. He felt an uncomfortable lump like a cold stone in his chest when she talked about the farm. Life had been the same for him and Mavis. All but for the kids. They had none to miss. He didn't know quite what to say. He felt he was expected to say something but all he could think of was, "No, life ain't easy for none of us."

"I know," she replied, almost mischievously, "that's why I'm so glad I'm done with it."

Harold shifted uneasily in his chair, jerked it backward, clanking Mavis' chair as he did so. "So ya feel lucky tonight do ya?" He tried to change the subject. He was secretly afraid that she might drop dead right in front of him. They said old folk could do that sort of thing, kind of will themselves to die. That wasn't the kind of excitement he was looking for. The thought spooked him.

"I don't *feel* lucky, young man. I have it on the best and highest authority that I will win the jackpot tonight." She rolled her sallow eyes upward and sat silent for a moment as if she could see through the clouds, through even the stars.

She was serious, Harold could tell, dead serious. Lord, how did he ever manage to get himself tangled up with these people. Awkwardly, he clamped his fingers round his styrofoam cup and said, "Well, I guess I'll get another cup before he starts up again." He looked over at Mavis who did not respond at all but sat, it seemed to Harold, like a lady chipped from ice. Humiliated, he turned to the old woman. "You want one?" he asked sheepishly.

"Why thank you so much for thinking of me but I don't drink it no more," she replied politely. Harold felt like a gentleman. Must bother her stomach, he thought. The old ones can't take too much of that sort of thing. He had a thought that maybe she might have a drink of warm milk after she got home tonight, but somehow that didn't fit either.

Harold arrived back at his table just as the caller returned to the stage. He pretended to hurry to make himself ready for the jackpot bingo—a total blackout. Every single slot on the card had to be shut. He hoped the old woman would think he had no time to talk. She didn't speak.

The bingo began. Under the B, number ten; under the O, sixty-five; under the I, eighteen; G, fifty-five, number fifty-five. The caller droned on and on while each person at each chair flicked and flicked and flicked the numbers dark, blacking them out like days on a calendar. Harold noticed that the old woman played only one card this time and had pushed her other card to the side. He also noticed that she seemed to flick a number shut every time one was called. After twenty-three numbers, the caller remarked jokingly to the crowd, "Folks, if it really is your lucky night, you could do it with the next number. For $377.50, the grand jackpot, under the I—"

Harold didn't learn till later what number actually was called, for the old woman threw her hand into the air and shrieked, "Bingo! Bingo! Bingo!" before he had a chance to hear it. The number made no difference to him. His cards were only pocked here and there with a few shut slots.

"The lady says she has a bingo," said the caller evenly. "We'll just have one of the girls check that out, ladies and gentlemen. Do not clear your cards." He sounded sceptical and so was Harold, but Harold hoped—more than that, he wished so strongly he very nearly prayed that she had won the jackpot, that everything was in order.

A middle-aged woman marched toward them in a business-like manner, briskly. She whisked the card from the old woman's hand and began reading the numbers back to the caller. "B-10, O-65," and so on, all of them correct. Even Mavis began to regard the old woman with interest, almost with respect.

Harold was convinced the old woman had been right about her luck. So she had finally won, he thought, and then with some personal excitement and delight, he completed his thought—that a loser could win; just because you never won didn't mean you never could. And in his throat and chest the lump which had been lodged for the better part of the evening, ever since the talk about the farm, mysteriously dissolved and he began to feel hope, not much hope, true enough, but unmistakably hope for himself and for his life and for his very existence.

The woman who was checking the card came to the final number. She flicked the shutter open. Where there should have been a number, there was only a blank white space. The old woman sat quietly, smiling, her hands confidently folded in her lap. She didn't appear in the least nervous. The room hushed. Then the checker spoke. "There's a number missing on this card," she called out. "Could you give us the last number called."

The man at the front spoke dispassionately. "There's no such a thing as a blank in this game. Under the I, sixteen, ma'am was the last number called. No bingo. All right ladies and gentlemen," he continued without pause, "for $377.50, under the N, thirty-five, N number thirty-five."

Harold looked up at the electronic scoreboard. I-16 all right. The machine couldn't be wrong. Must have been a mistake at the printing plant, he thought. That sort of thing happened every so often. But why hadn't the old lady seen it. She said she'd played bingo all her life. She should have known there was no such a thing as a blank. But then the old ones couldn't always see so well, he thought—or the young ones either for that matter. He had trouble keeping track himself.

"No!" the old woman cried out. "It was under the I-Zero that was called. I know it, sure as I'm sitting here. I was supposed to win. I did win." She was near to tears and so was Harold for that matter. Moreover he was angry. What kind of luck is that, he thought; a blank space for God's sake. They should have let her have it, just this once.

The caller looked up and out toward the old woman. "Ma'am," he said, "even if there was such a thing as a zero in the game it would be under the B, not the I." There was a roar of laughter from the crowd.

Meanwhile, the woman who had checked the card was trying to explain, rationally, but the old lady wouldn't listen. "No! No!" she said and she thumped her frail fist on the plywood table. "It ain't fair!" Harold watched helplessly as the old woman wept, sniffling into the unravelling embroidered roses of her yellowed hankie. Harold was embarrassed for her. He had thought she was stronger. He reconsidered his thought about the strength of will the old ones were supposed to have. Now he guessed it wasn't so.

People nearby were glaring at the old woman now. Some, including Mavis, were making shushing noises which sounded like the angry oblique whispers people made when a baby was crying in a crowded theatre. They couldn't hear the caller, they said—"The old bat probably can't see her hand in front of her face, shouldn't be here anyway," someone said.

Harold was sure she heard that remark. She immediately

straightened herself, wiped her nose one last time, picked up her bag and rose proudly, effortlessly, he thought, for a woman her age.

She turned to leave; then as if to spite the hostile players around her and at the same time to comfort Harold, she glanced back at him and said clearly in a thin but loud voice, "All right then, so be it. But I'll be back next week. I won't rest till I win." With that, she shuffle-glided between the tables and out the doorway.

"Good riddance," Mavis snapped.

Harold regarded his wife incredulously, as if he had never seen her before. He felt badly for the old lady. He was no longer interested in his cards, not even for appearances' sake. The more he thought about it, the more unfair the whole thing seemed to him, and that feeling grew to include not only the bingo but finally the whole world. She did have spunk after all, he thought, said she'd be back and he bet she would too. She was a woman who'd been through a lot. A little setback like this wouldn't stop her.

Finally, someone yelled "Bingo!" and the blackout was over. Harold thought the guy who won that one took dirty money. Harold himself wouldn't have taken a cent of that money home.

Mavis efficiently cleared and stacked her nine cards beside her and was spreading out the Bonanza cards when Harold turned to her and said, "I guess I'll go start the truck, get her warmed up."

Mavis looked up and nodded. "Better put on your cap then," she said. He reached under the table and fetched his cap. He put it on and pulled the fleece flaps down over his ears. Then he left.

On his way out he remembered the paralyzing cold and wondered how the old lady made out in this kind of weather. Because almost everyone played the Bonanza cards, the stairway was deserted but for a few of the menfolk who were on their way down to the bar in the Legion basement. Halfway down the stairs, Harold looked out through the plate glass doors at the bottom of the landing. He stopped for a moment, then muttered to himself, but out loud, "Jesus, it *is* her." He could see the body of the old woman crumpled on the ground just a few yards from the door. He could see her pink hat laying beside her.

He ran down the stairs and heaving his shoulder against the doors, spread them easily. He lumbered through the drifting snow.

The wind had already begun to sting red blotches on his face and hands by the time he got there. When he knelt down on one Khaki knee beside the body, his leg sunk deep into the snow. He found the old woman motionless, undisciplined spittle running slowly out of her slack blue mouth, her hollow eyes rolled up toward the snowflakes driven like tiny arrows in the Legion light. She was dead.

He lifted the plastic handbag out of one half-open hand, gloved in pink angora. He opened the bag. Identification, he thought. He took out a billfold, snapped it open and held a card up to the light. It was an old age pension card. An address was what he was looking for, someone to call—there it was in finely typed letters—Mrs. Bertha Louise McNaughton, Pine Mountain Lodge, 1632 - 13 Avenue N.W. There was a phone number, 358-6924.

On the way to the hall, Harold's mind flicked back to the bingo, to his fear that she might drop dead. He had been right about that, he thought. Goddammit if she didn't do just that. But he had been wrong about the loss of the jackpot not bothering her. He should have known, maybe should have gone after her, talked to her. A stroke, likely, or a heart attack maybe, he thought. Too worked up. The old ones can't take it. Harold suddenly felt guilty, sick and guilty.

He stamped his workboots mechanically two or three times on the coco mat at the door. When he got to the pay phone near the entrance, he took out his Exports, tapped one out and lit it, coughing badly. He spit on the floor and took a drag from the cigarette. His hand shook. He took a dime out of his pocket, dropped it into the slot of the phone, and hearing the buzz at the end of the line, he dialed the number for the lodge.

"Good evening, Pine Mountain Lodge, Matron Benstone speaking."

"Ya," stammered Harold, "ah, this is Harold Sampson here. I'm at the Legion Hall up on Southmount, at the bingo, like, and I found an old woman in the parking lot here. I think she's dead—must've had a heart attack or somethin'. Her I.D. says she lives there at the lodge. Name's Mrs. Bertha McNaughton, it says. Should I call an ambulance, er —ah what should I do. Maybe you should send somebody down."

There was a long silence at the other end of the line. Then the voice said, quietly, "Ah—thank you very much for calling us, Mr. Sampson, but Mrs. McNaughton couldn't be there. You see she did pass away—of a heart attack—there, last week after the bingo. As a matter of fact her funeral is on Saturday afternoon at the Legion Hall. Are you sure it's Mrs. McNaughton?" There followed another even longer silence than the first.

Then Harold said, "Ya, ya, I'm pretty sure, I think. Can you hold on a minute. I'll just go check. Hold on, will ya." Harold dropped the receiver and heard the voice from the dangling apparatus reassure him, "Yes Mr. Sampson, certainly I'll hold." He was already to the plate glass doors.

He cupped his hands over his eyes and squinted toward the parking lot, staring hard at that spot in the parking lot where the body was supposed to be. It was no longer there. Harold pushed open the door and ran to the spot. Still there was no body, no hat, no bag. There wasn't even the indentation from his knee. Frightened, Harold glanced at the sky, expecting something—he didn't know what. There was nothing, only the flick flick of tiny snow arrows in the Legion Light.

He ran back into the hall. People were pouring noisily down the stairway and out the doors. He stamped his feet on the mat, scraping them backward, flinging snow against the doorsill. He loped through the crowd to the phone, grabbed the dangling receiver and almost shouted into it. "Must have been a mistake. I guess so. Sorry to bother you."

"That's perfectly all right, Mr. Sampson. You're sure everything is all right?"

"Ya, it's ok. It's ok."

"Goodbye then, Mr. Sampson."

"Goodbye." Harold replaced the receiver.

His eyes fell on the bulletin board which was directly to his right beside the pay phone. There it was. The second announcement. That was why the name had sounded so familiar to him. He felt slightly relieved. Yet, as he stood listlessly waiting for Mavis, he began to realize that nothing really was explained at all. Except maybe that he had been right in the first place about the will of the old ones, more right than he wanted to be.

He longed desperately to tell someone about it, to tell someone that something very special had happened to him. But who? Mavis? She would think he had finally lost all his marbles. Of all people, she would understand the least. The fellas at the plant? No, they would laugh, say, "Old Harold always was a joker. You sure can tell some tall ones, Harold. You should write 'em down some day. Make a million."

Besides, and this was what bothered Harold the most, maybe he was losing his grip on things. Harold was afraid of those who were, as they said, touched. And he knew that no matter how bad things were now, no matter how boring and stale and tedious his life had been, things could get worse. He had learned that along the way. So he set his mind to never telling anyone about it.

He reached into his parka pocket where he had stuffed the old age pension card. He would tear it up, he thought, throw it away. But no matter how deeply he shoved his hand into the pocket, no matter how he fumbled, all he could come up with was a half-empty match packet, a shirt button and a small wad of lint.

Now he was even more frightened, had never been so

afraid in his life. The worst of it was it showed on his face. When Mavis came up to him, the first thing she said was, "My God, Harol', you look like you seen a ghost. What's the matter?"

"Nothin'," said Harold. "let's go. You ready?" He lit another Export.

"Ya, I'm ready." Mavis was smiling. "I won the Bonanza! $78.75! Did you hear that Harol'? You shoulda been there." Her face was flushed, red-mottled. She wore a crooked, self-satisfied smile and she was excitely twisting and folding and carressing the paper money with her thick, short-fingered hands. "And no one else bingoed, Harol'. I didn't have to share a cent. Well, when that guy called out my last number, I yelled 'Bingo!' then and there. First thing tomorrow morning I'm going down to the Betty Shop and see if I can't find myself a new coat, one of them imitation moutons or—"

"That's fine, Mavis, just fine," Harold interrupted weakly.

"I hope you're not coming down with the 'flu, Harol'. That's all we need." Her tone of voice had changed already.

"Could be," said Harold, "I don't feel too good all right." All the warmth seemed to have left his body. He shivered uncontrollably now. His yellow teeth clattered and clicked without his consent. His lips were dry.

They didn't speak again until they were in the truck, half-way home. At the last set of lights on Southmount, he finally said it, quietly, "I'm tellin' you right now Mavis, so's you'll know for good an' for all—wild horses couldn't drag me to another goddamn bingo game."

Harold riveted his eyes to the windshield, to the spray and hiss of flakes against the glass. Mavis snapped her head toward him, flung her face close to his, spitting words, "You never could stand me havin' a good time, could you Harol'? Could you Harol'?"

Penny in
the Dust

My sister and I were walking through the old sun-still fields the evening before my father's funeral, recalling this memory or that—trying, after the fashion of families who gather again in the place where they were born, to identify ourselves with the strange children we must have been.

"Do you remember the afternoon we thought you were lost?" my sister said. I did. That was as long ago as the day I was seven, but I'd had occasion to remember it only yesterday.

"We searched everywhere," she said. "Up in the meeting-house, back in the blueberry barrens—we even looked in the well. I think it's the only time I ever saw Father really upset. He didn't even stop to take the oxen off the wagon tongue when they told him. He raced right through the chopping where Tom Reeve was burning brush, looking for you—right through the flames almost; they couldn't do a thing with him. And you up in your bed, sound asleep!"

ERNEST
BUCKLER

"It was all over losing a penny or something, wasn't it?" she went on, when I didn't answer. It was. She laughed indulgently. "You were a crazy kid, weren't you."

I was. But there was more to it than that. I had never seen a shining new penny before that day. I'd thought they were all black. This one was bright as gold. And my father had given it to me.

You would have to understand about my father, and that is the hard thing to tell. If I say that he worked all day long but never once had I seen him hurry, that would make him sound like a stupid man. If I say that he never held me on his knee when I was a child and that I never heard him laugh out loud in his life, it would make him sound humourless and severe. If I said that whenever I'd be reeling off some of my fanciful plans and he'd come into the kitchen and I'd stop short, you'd think that he was distant and that in some kind of way I was afraid of him. None of that would be true.

There's no way you can tell it to make it sound like anything more than an inarticulate man a little at sea with an imaginative child. You'll have to take my word for it that there was more to it than that. It was as if his sure-footed way in the fields forsook him the moment he came near the door of my child's world and that he could never intrude on it without feeling awkward and conscious of trespass; and that I, sensing that but not understanding it, felt at the sound of his solid step outside, the child-world's foolish fragility. He would fix the small spot where I planted beans and other quick-sprouting seeds before he prepared the big garden, even if the spring was late; but he wouldn't ask me how many rows I wanted and if he made three rows and I wanted four, I couldn't ask him to change them. If I walked behind the load of hay, longing to ride, and he walked ahead of the oxen, I couldn't ask him to put me up and he wouldn't make any move to do so until he saw me trying to grasp the binder.

He, my father, had just given me a new penny, bright as gold.

He'd taken it from his pocket several times, pretending to examine the date on it, waiting for me to notice it. He couldn't offer me *anything* until I had shown some sign that the gift would be welcome.

"You can have it if you want it, Pete," he said at last.

"Oh, thanks," I said. Nothing more. I couldn't expose any of my eagerness either.

I started with it, to the store. For a penny you could buy the magic cylinder of "Long Tom" popcorn with Heaven knows what glittering bauble inside. But the more I thought of my bright penny disappearing forever into the black drawstring pouch the storekeeper kept his money in, the slower my steps lagged as the store came nearer and nearer. I sat down in the road.

It was that time of magic suspension in an August afternoon. The lifting smells of leaves and cut clover hung still in the sun. The sun drowsed, like a kitten curled up on my shoulder. The deep flour-fine dust in the road puffed about my bare ankles, warm and soft as sleep. The sound of the cowbells came sharp and hollow from the cool swamp.

I began to play with the penny, putting off the decision. I would close my eyes and bury it deep in the sand; and then, with my eyes still closed, get up and walk around, and then come back to search for it. Tantalizing myself, each time, with the excitement of discovering afresh its bright shining edge. I did that again and again. Alas, once too often.

It was almost dark when their excited talking in the room awakened me. It was Mother who had found me. I suppose when it came dusk she thought of me in my bed other nights, and I suppose she looked there without any reasonable hope but only as you look in every place where the thing that is lost has ever lain before. And now suddenly she was crying because when she opened the door there, miraculously, I was.

"Peter!" she cried, ignoring the obvious in her sudden relief, "*where* have you been?"

"I lost my penny," I said.

"You lost your penny ... ? But what made you come up here and hide?"

If Father hadn't been there, I might have told her the whole story. But when I looked up at Father, standing there like the shape of everything sound and straight, it was like daylight shredding the memory of a silly dream. How could I bear the shame of repeating before him the childish visions I had built in my head in the magic August afternoon when almost anything could be made to seem real, as I buried the penny and dug it up again? How could I explain that pit-of-the-stomach sickness which struck through the whole day when I had to believe, at last, that it was really gone? How could I explain that I wasn't really hiding from *them*? How, with the words and the understanding I had then, that this was the only possible place to run from that awful feeling of loss?

"I lost my penny," I said again. I looked at Father and turned my face into the pillow. "I want to go to sleep."

"Peter," Mother said. "It's almost nine o'clock. You haven't had a bite of supper. Do you know you almost scared the *life* out of us?"

"You better get some supper," Father said. It was the only time he had spoken.

I never dreamed that he would mention the thing again. But the next morning when we had the hay forks in our hands, ready to toss out the clover, he seemed to postpone the moment of actually leaving for the field. He stuck his fork in the ground and brought in another pail of water, though the kettle was chock full. He took out the shingle nail that held a broken yoke strap together and put it back in exactly the same hole. He went into the shed to see if the pigs had cleaned up all their breakfast.

And then he said abruptly: "Ain't you got no idea where you lost your penny?"

"Yes," I said, "I know just about."

"Let's see if we can't find it," he said.

We walked down the road together, stiff with awareness.

He didn't hold my hand.

"It's right here somewhere," I said. "I was playin' with it, in the dust."

He looked at me, but he didn't ask me what game anyone could possibly play with a penny in the dust.

I might have known he would find it. He could tap the alder bark with his jackknife just exactly hard enough so it wouldn't split but so it would twist free from the notched wood, to make a whistle. His great fingers could trace loose the hopeless snarl of a fishing line that I could only succeed in tangling tighter and tighter. If I broke the handle of my wheelbarrow ragged beyond sight of any possible repair, he could take it and bring it back to me so you could hardly see the splice if you weren't looking for it.

He got down on his knees and drew his fingers carefully through the dust, like a harrow; not clawing it frantically into heaps as I had done, covering even as I uncovered. He found the penny almost at once.

He held it in his hand, as if the moment of passing it to me were a deadline for something he dreaded to say, but must. Something that could not be put off any longer, if it were to be spoken at all.

"Pete," he said, "you needn'ta hid. I wouldn'ta beat you."

Beat me? Oh, Father! You didn't think that was the reason . . . ? I felt almost sick. I felt as if I had struck *him*.

I had to tell him the truth then. Because only the truth, no matter how ridiculous it was, would have the unmistakable sound truth has, to scatter that awful idea out of his head.

"I wasn't hidin', Father," I said, "honest. I was. . . . I was buryin' my penny and makin' out I was diggin' up treasure. I was makin' out I was findin' gold. I didn't know what to *do* when I lost it, I just didn't know where to *go*. . . ." His head was bent forward, like mere listening. I had to make it truer still.

"I made out it was gold," I said desperately, "and I—I was makin' out I bought you a mowin' machine so's you could get your work done early every day so's you and I could go in to town in the big automobile I made out I bought you—and everyone'd turn around and look at us drivin' down the streets. . . ." His head was perfectly still, as if he were only waiting with patience for me to finish. "*Laugh*in' and *talk*in'," I said. Louder, smiling intensely, com*pell*ing him, by the absolute conviction of some true particular, to believe me.

He looked up then. It was the only time I had ever seen tears in his eyes. It was the only time in my seven years that he had ever put his arm around me.

I wondered, though, why he hesitated, and then put the penny back in his own pocket.

Yesterday I knew. I never found any fortune and we never had a car to ride in together. But I think he knew what that would be like, just the same. I found the penny again yesterday, when we were getting out his good suit—in an upper vest pocket where no one ever carries change. It was still shining. He must have kept it polished.

I left it there.

Heyfitz

An anonymous man, let us call him Franz, discovers one day that he has been fatally wounded. He decides to approach his end in a languorous way, and dresses himself in dark trousers, blue silk shirt, a mustache he has found by the washstand.

In his fatal moment, twilight is his time. He lies in the arms of a beautiful anonymous woman and he prepares to confess. "God," he says, "have I ever asked you any favors before?"

He sinks deep into the arms of his beloved. One more time? Why not. Records change, the sun sinks lower into the hills, all else remains posted.

Afterward Franz washes himself carefully, but finds his wound has still not gone away. He prepares to look in the mirror, to see in his aging and tragic face the most hopeless of all creatures. Instead he discovers that it is two weeks since he has shaved. At that moment, Franz realizes he need fear no wound, no matter how fatal, for he has never existed.

MATT
COHEN

Franz woke up hearing voices. Even his name had a familiar ring.

"Franz?" called his wife.

"Yes?"

"Do you want to speak on the telephone?"

It was while putting the receiver to his ear that Franz looked down and saw that his wound remained, unchanged.

"Franz," said a stranger's voice. "How are you enjoying your vacation?" From the kitchen, Franz could hear the sounds of eggs breaking against the iron skillet. It reminded him of the sea.

"Very well," Franz said. "Very well."

"We hope you will soon return," said the voice. Franz put his hand over the mouthpiece and scratched at his beard. The Spanish sun slanted in the window and blinded him. Or was it Spain? It might have been Italy.

"Franz," said the voice. "I'm talking to you."

"Yes." It was too late for disguises. "You'll have to excuse me," Franz said, and placed the receiver back on the hook. Then he walked into the kitchen and sat down in front of his breakfast. Dolores his wife was named, dolorous. He sometimes liked to make jokes about her name: his favorite was that he had met her at a funeral, where she was employed as a professional mourner.

"Franz," she said.

"Yes?"

"Are you feeling better?"

"Was I sick?"

"Of course not," his wife said. "Who ever told you you were sick?" She looked at him. He looked at her. They often liked to try to fool each other this way. It was also one of their games. Another: to stand on the balcony, wrapped in a towel, disguised as a politician speaking to the masses. Yet another: to cook each other little mystery dinners dressed in scalloped potatoes and Chinese lettuce. They looked at each other. Franz thought he knew what was going on in his wife's mind. He thought she was looking at him and thinking: Franz, this is good-by. I'm so sorry you're sick. I'll live forever, whereas for you, I'm afraid, this is good-by. He could imagine her at his funeral. She was, after all, a professional.

"Franz?" she said.

"Yes."

"Who are you? Really?"

"Who are you?" he returned.

"I'll tell you later," said Dolores. Was she bluffing?

They looked at each other. Franz scratched his nose, expecting to find his false mustache. But it had fallen off during the night and now Franz was left alone.

When Franz returned to the city, two months had passed. His wound had grown into an illness, and one afternoon he found himself in the office of a famous doctor.

"How do you feel?" asked the doctor.

"Sick."

Franz was sitting on the consulting table, his long white shirt hanging modestly to his knees. The doctor stood in front of him, looking at him absently, as if he were an X-ray photograph.

"What are your symptoms?"

"They're hard to describe," Franz said. "I feel pains in different places. Sometimes I wake up and am sore all over. Other times I don't wake up at all; I sleep right through."

"Through what?" asked the doctor. He had a voice that cannot be described.

"I don't know," Franz said. "That's just it. I feel I'm missing something." He looked hopelessly at the doctor. A new suspicion was entering his mind. "Are you working for my wife?"

"No," said the doctor sharply, in his indescribable voice.

"I was just testing you," Franz said. He laughed. It was the first time he had laughed in two months, for on the morning of the telephone conversation his wife had left him without even doing the dishes.

"Do I pass the test?" asked the doctor.

"Of course," Franz said. "If you weren't going to pass, I wouldn't have invented you."

The eminent doctor stroked his chin. He began tapping at Franz's knees with a small rubber hammer. He took his temperature, his blood pressure, made him piss into a bottle.

"Do you know what's wrong with you?" the doctor finally asked.

"No," said Franz. Although he had his own ideas. The doctor put on his glasses and prepared to give his diagnosis. The door opened. In came a nurse. Before either of them could protest, she began to disrobe in an unobtrusive way. At the last moment Franz realized that this was his own wife. The doctor had fooled him after all.

"What are you doing here?"

"Oh, it's you," she said, pretending to be surprised.

They used to have different games. For example: the first time he stayed away for a week, he came home to find Dolores drunk, in the bathtub with a stranger. She had forgotten to run the water. The stranger was a new cat. "Hello," she said when she opened her eyes; and acted as if he had never left. Nothing he said could make her admit something unusual had happened.

Another example: one day she was telling him about her former lovers—at his insistence. He was growing increasingly uncomfortable and jealous. To console himself he put on his false mustache and began to smoke a cigar. "I have to tell you this," she whispered. "Joseph Stalin used to take baths in pickle juice in order to preserve himself." At this unfortunate moment one of Franz's mistresses arrived in the dumbwaiter, wearing a compromising costume.

A final example: the cat was always changing. One week it was tabby, the next Persian, the next Siamese, et cetera. Neither of them would admit to changing the cat, yet they never had the same cat twice. It always answered to the name of Heyfitz.

"Heyfitz," Franz would say.

The cat would look at him.

"Heyfitz, today I'm going to teach you how to juggle."
Franz believed that it would be unusual to have a juggling
cat. He had even found out the true secret of successful
juggling: it is to keep the eye on the top ball. Sometimes he
would succeed in teaching Heyfitz the first elementary
maneuvers. But then the week would end, and Heyfitz would
be changed.

It should be said that Franz was completely taken in by
this particular game. He was so surprised by it each week
that he never once said good-by, and there finally came a
time when he believed Dolores could change cats in the
dark.

"I'll tell you what you have," the doctor said. They were
alone again and it was twilight. All signs of the struggle had
been erased by the setting sun and Franz felt an obscure
victorious warmth creeping through his belly. Of course he
had dressed again. He and the doctor were sitting in the
famous man's library, looking over a few medical texts from
the Dark Ages.

"The trouble with you," said the doctor, "is that you
invented yourself. As is common in such delusions, you
began to believe you invented others, too. Your wife, for
example."

"Oh, no," Franz said. "I wouldn't have invented her."

"So you say," said the doctor.

To pass the time, they began to play a game of chess. As
Franz was elongating the Sicilian Defense—or perhaps it
was only a variation of the Italian Opening—he saw that a
cat had entered the room. "Heyfitz," he said. The cat jumped
into his lap. The doctor looked at him suspiciously.

"You see?" the doctor said. "You invented that cat."

"No, I didn't. I never saw it before."

Heyfitz stretched slowly, then went over to the buffet and
began to juggle three small oranges.

"That's amazing," the doctor admitted. He became extremely demoralized. His play deteriorated, slid downhill; moves followed each other like badly rolled cigarettes. Soon Franz had the eminent doctor trapped in a deep cul-de-sac from which there was no escape.

"I'm afraid it's all over for you," said Franz, surveying the board.

"Not for me," the doctor said. "I have to tell you one more thing." He looked at Franz darkly. "If you're not inventing me, I must be inventing you. Ha ha." He reached down and had a brilliant stroke. "Checkmate," he said indescribably.

The next morning, Franz's illness was worse: he discovered that he was turning into himself. He stared at his face in the mirror: his eyes, blankly burning, stared back, waiting to be released. It was almost three months since he had shaved. He scratched his beard and brushed his teeth.

"Heyfitz," Franz called.

The cat came into the bathroom. This week it was Persian, with long white fur.

"Heyfitz," Franz said. "Who do I remind you of?" Heyfitz looked at him carefully, shrugged his white shoulders and walked out.

"All right," Franz said. "I know what you mean." He dressed himself in a dark suit, a white shirt, and a tie. He combed back his thinning hair and put on his sunglasses. Before going outside he made himself a cup of coffee and looked out the window of his apartment. Rivers of traffic passed each other by. Dozens of people stood out on the street, oblivious to everything except the feel of the morning sun on their faces. Franz opened the window. The air rushed in: a mixture of exhaust fumes, restaurant smells, late-summer flowers, flesh wet and powdered for the day.

"All right," Franz said again. "I know what you mean." He turned back to the room. While he was looking out the window Heyfitz had been changed. He was now a lazy black cat with thick glossy fur.

"Heyfitz," Franz said.

The cat blinked.

"You could have fooled me," Franz said. He felt that the situation was deteriorating. "I hope you'll excuse me," he said to Heyfitz. "But I don't have time to teach you how to juggle. Keep your eye on the top ball." On the way out the door, he looked in the mirror once more: eyes, lips, nose— even the lines on his forehead—everything was exactly in place, exactly as it should be, exactly *him*.

Franz closed the door behind him and walked down the stairs and out onto the street. His apartment was above a small grocery store. Placed outside it were wooden crates of fruits and vegetables, their skins glistening green, red, yellow, lighting up the shadows like wet jewels. The owner of the store was standing beside his produce, spraying it against the day's heat. He nodded at Franz without speaking. Franz nodded back, also without speaking. It was their only game.

With his hands in his pockets, Franz began to walk down the street. Cars, store windows, people, telephone poles, dogs—all swept by in a confused flood. When he got hot, Franz bought an ice cream cone and stood in the shade of a striped awning. With his dark suit, his undone tie, his short thinning hair, Franz looked like a professional mourner. "Dolores," Franz said. She had often dressed up as him, putting on one of his suits and hiding in a cupboard to surprise him. Now, finally, when it was too late, he was returning the favor. "Dolores," Franz said again. A warm victorious feeling crept into his stomach. Somehow he had swallowed her without meaning to.

It was high noon in the city. The sun shone desperately, trying to reach through the pavement, the underground pipes and sewers, the subways that had never been completed—trying to reach through the smoke, and the dirt, and the toys of the city, to the earth. It didn't succeed. Franz finished his cone and wiped his mouth against his coat. It was a poor day to be wearing a suit, but the occasion was special.

"Heyfitz," Franz said. He looked around. He had finally realized that they were using Heyfitz to follow him.

Franz resumed his walk. In a few minutes he had reached his objective, the university: it was a tall gray building that stretched sixty stories up into the air. The lobby was veneered with black spotted marble and elevator doors. Each of the sixty floors of the university represented an entire realm of man's existence; and of course they were completely separate from each other. But Franz didn't go to any of them. Instead he descended the stairs into the basement and made his way through the irregular corridors.

Presently he encountered a small stooped man who was pushing a broom along the granite floor. Over his shoulder he carried a small sack filled with a day's supply of Dustbane.

"How are you doing?" Franz asked.

"I can't complain," said the old man. He leaned the broom against the wall and examined his son. "What's wrong with you?"

"I don't know," Franz began. Then he saw what the old man was staring at. "I decided to grow a beard."

The old man shook his head and muttered, as if he had heard this a thousand times before. He took out a stub of a cigarette and lit it.

"I thought you were going to stop smoking," Franz said.

"How is your wife?" the old man asked in a sly voice.

"Well," Franz began.

"Tell me later." The old man took Franz by the elbow and gently led him to a deserted corner of the corridor, where they found some old wooden chairs and a kettle. The old man chopped up one of the chairs and started a fire while Franz filled the kettle from a nearby fountain.

When their tea was boiled, the old man smiled at Franz and signaled him to begin again. They looked alike, these two men: father and son. One was older, of course. And the other had a beard.

"It was at the doctor's," Franz said. "There was an accident." He looked into the eyes of his father. They were the color of burnished eggplant. "There was a game we used to play," said Franz. "One of us would stand at the open window and say to the other—Mother, push me." Telling his father this reminded Franz of other games they used to play together, in the bathtub. "She's still around," Franz said helplessly. "She's still changing the cat." His father blinked sympathetically at him.

"I'm sick," Franz admitted. "I don't feel right these days. Things seem to be going out of control. Do you ever get that feeling?" His hands began to tremble and he spilled his cup of tea. "God-damn smoke," Franz said. He kicked the fire apart. "Why don't they ventilate this place properly?" He looked at his father. His father looked back, sadly. It was years since they had seen each other. If they had had any games, they had forgotten them. "Heyfitz," Franz called. "HEYFITZ!" He looked around desperately. Nothing. He handed his empty cup back to his father. "I'm sorry," he said. "I have to go. Good-by." He looked at his father, snapped his fingers nervously, then ran down the corridor until he found his way to the stairs.

Outside, Franz felt worse than ever. It was hot. The afternoon was filled with vapors and smoke. He took off his jacket and laid it on a bench. Then he started home, walking and running, his breath so short that by the time he got to the grocery store his lungs were burning and his ribs felt as if they were tearing apart.

The owner was still wearing his white smock, still standing in front of his fruits and vegetables, keeping them freshly wet. He nodded at Franz. Franz nodded at him.

"What happened to your eggplants?" Franz said. This was

a new ploy. He had never spoken to the man before.

The grocer laughed. "Eggplants? I never had any."

"All right," Franz said aggressively. "I was only asking." He paused. Now that they were talking, anything could happen.

"Have you seen my wife?" asked Franz.

"Is she missing? What happened to her?"

"Nothing," Franz said. Their first silence had been broken. Their second silence now began. It was empty. Franz nodded. The grocer nodded back. "See you later," Franz said.

The grocer refused to reply.

Franz went up the stairs and into the apartment. As soon as he was inside, he locked the door and went into the bathroom to inspect himself in the mirror. His eyes glowed, his beard was growing full, his hair had receded farther, leaving intimations of a skull. Inside his chest he could feel his heart beating, trapped by his ribs. He looked at himself. Pounding heart, burning eyes: somehow they had gone out of control. A new possibility entered his brain. "What if I exist?" Franz asked himself. "What if I am?" He remembered the first game he had ever played with his wife. They had taken off all their clothes and pretended they were strangers. He put his hand to his chest. He could feel his heart struggling like a dying animal.

"Heyfitz," he called. "Heyfitz."

No one appeared.

Franz went into the living room. "Heyfitz," he called. A noise made him turn around. In the corner was standing the eminent doctor, wrapped in a glossy black fur coat and juggling three oranges. He looked at Franz sadly. On the window sill was crouched the shadow of Dolores, not quite hidden by the setting sun.

"Heyfitz," called Franz. The doctor was wearing a black velvet hat and his eyes shone out like wet yellow jewels.

"All right," Franz said. "I know what you mean."

Jorinda and Jorindel

A summer night: all night someone has been learning the Charleston.

"I've got it!" the dancer cries. "I've got it, everybody. Watch me, now!" But no one is watching. The dancer is alone in the dining room, clinging to the handle of the door; the rest of the party is in the living room, across the hall. "Watch me!" travels unheard over the quiet lawn and the silent lake, and then dissolves.

The walls of the summer house are thin. The doors have been thrown back and the windows pushed as high as they will go. Young Irmgard wakes up with her braids undone and her thumb in her mouth. She has been dreaming about her cousin Bradley; about an old sidewalk with ribbon grass growing in the cracks. "I've got it," cried the witch who had captured Jorinda, and she reached out so as to catch Jorindel and change him into a bird.

MAVIS
GALLANT

Poor Mrs. Bloodworth is learning to dance. She holds the handle of the dining-room door and swivels her feet in satin shoes, but when she lets go the handle, she falls down flat on her behind and stays that way, sitting, her hair all over her face, her feet pointing upward in her new shoes. Earlier, Mrs. Bloodworth was sitting that way, alone, when, squinting through her hair, she saw Irmgard sitting in her nightgown on the stairs. "Are you watching the fun?" she said in a tragic voice. "Is it really you, my sweet pet?" And she got to her feet and crawled up the stairs on her hands and knees to kiss Irmgard with ginny breath.

There is prohibition where Mrs. Bloodworth comes from. She has come up to Canada for a party; she came up for just one weekend and never went away. The party began as a wedding in Montreal, but it has been days since anyone mentioned the bride and groom. The party began in Montreal, came down to the lake, and now has dwindled to five: Irmgard's mother and father, Mrs. Bloodworth, Mrs. Bloodworth's friend Bill, and the best man, who came up for the wedding from Buffalo. "Darling pet, may I always stay?" said Mrs. Bloodworth, sobbing, her arms around Irmgard's mother's neck. Why she was sobbing this way nobody knows; she is always crying, dancing, embracing her friends.

In the morning Mrs. Bloodworth will be found in the hammock outside. The hammock smells of fish, the pillow is stuffed with straw; but Mrs. Bloodworth can never be made to go to bed. Irmgard inspects her up and down, from left to right. It isn't every morning of the year that you find a large person helplessly asleep. She is still wearing her satin shoes. Her eyeballs are covered with red nets. When she wakes up she seems still asleep, until she says stickily, "I'm having a rotten time, I don't care what anybody says." Irmgard backs off and then turns and runs along the gallery—the veranda, Mrs. Bloodworth would say—and up the side of the house and into the big kitchen, where behind screen doors Mrs. Queen and Germaine are drinking tea. They are drinking it in silence, for Germaine does not understand one word of

English and Mrs. Queen is certainly not going to learn any French.

Germaine is Irmgard's *bonne d'enfant*. They have been together about a century, and have a history stuffed with pageants, dangers, near escapes. Germaine has been saving Irmgard for years and years; but now Irmgard is nearly eight, and there isn't much Germaine can do except iron her summer dresses and braid her hair. They know a separation is near; and Irmgard is cheeky now, as she never was in the past; and Germaine pretends there have been other children she has liked just as well. She sips her tea. Irmgard drops heavily on her lap, joggling the cup. She will never be given anything even approaching Germaine's unmeasured love again. She leans heavily on her and makes her spill her tea. Germaine is mild and simple, a little dull. You can be rude and impertinent if necessary, but she must never be teased.

Germaine remembers the day Irmgard was kidnapped. When she sees a warm August morning like this one, she remembers that thrilling day. There was a man in a motor-car who wanted to buy Irmgard ice cream. She got in the car and it started moving, and suddenly there came Germaine running behind, with her mouth open and her arms wide, and Molly, the collie they had in those days, running with her ears back and her eyes slits. "Stop for Molly!" Irmgard suddenly screamed, and she turned and threw up all over the man's coat. "*Le matin du kidnap*," Germaine begins softly. It is a good thing she is here to recall the event, because the truth is that Irmgard remembers nothing about that morning at all.

Mrs. Queen is standing up beside the stove. She never sits down to eat, because she wants them to see how she hasn't a minute to waste; she is on the alert every second. Mrs. Queen is not happy down at the lake. It is not what she expected by "a country place." When she worked for Lady Partridge things were otherwise; you knew what to expect by "a country place." Mrs. Queen came out to Canada with Lady Partridge. The wages were low, and she had no stomach for travel, but she was devoted to Lady P. and to Ty-Ty and Buffy, the two cairns. The cairns died, because of the change of air, and after Lady P. had buried them, she went out to her daughter in California, leaving Mrs. Queen to look after the graves. But Mrs. Queen has never taken to Canada. She can't get used to it. She cannot get used to a place where the railway engines are that size and make that kind of noise, and where the working people are as tall as anyone else. When Mrs. Queen was interviewing Irmgard's mother, to see if Irmgard's mother would do, she said she had never taken to the place and couldn't promise a thing. The fancy might take her any minute to turn straight around and go back to England. She had told Lady Partridge the same thing. "When was that, Mrs. Queen?" "In nineteen ten, in the spring." She has never felt at home, and never wants to, and never will. If you ask her why she is unhappy, she says it is because of Ty-Ty and Buffy, the cairns; and because this is a paltry rented house and a paltry kitchen; and she is glad that Ty-Ty and Buffy are peacefully in their graves.

The party last night kept Mrs. Queen awake. She had to get up out of her uncomfortable bed and let the collies out of the garage. They knew there was a party somewhere, and were barking like fools. She let them out, she says, and then spent some time on the gallery, looking in the living-room window. It was a hot, airless night. (She happens to have the only stuffy room in the house.) The party was singing "Little Joe." Apparently, she did not see Mrs. Bloodworth dancing and falling down; at least she doesn't mention it.

Mrs. Queen is not going to clean up the mess in the living room. It is not her line of country. She is sick, sore, and weary. Germaine will, if asked, but just now she is braiding Irmgard's hair. Eating toast, Irmgard leans comfortably against Germaine. They are perfectly comfortable with each other, but Mrs. Queen is crying over by the stove.

Irmgard's cousin Bradley went back to Boston yesterday. She should be missing him, but he has vanished, fallen out of

summer like a stone. He got on the train covered with bits of
tape and lotion, and with a patch on one eye. Bradley had a
terrible summer. He got poison ivy, in July, before coming
here. In August, he grew a sty, which became infected, and
then he strained his right arm. "I don't know what your
mother will say," Irmgard's mother said. At this, after a
whole summer of being without them, Bradley suddenly
remembered he had a father and mother, and started to cry.
Bradley is ten, but tall as eleven. He and Irmgard have the
same look—healthy and stubborn, like well-fed, intelligent
mice. They often stare in the mirror, side by side, positively
blown up with admiration. But Bradley is superior to Irmgard in every way. When you ask him what he wants to be,
he says straight off, "A mechanical and electrical engineer,"
whereas Irmgard is still hesitating between a veterinary and
a nun.

"Have you dropped Freddy now that Bradley is here?" It
seems that she was asked that a number of times.

"Oh, I still like Freddy, but Bradley's my cousin and
everything." This is a good answer. She has others, such as,
"I'm English-Canadian only I can talk French and I'm German descent on one side." (Bradley is not required to think
of answers; he is American, and that does. But in Canada you
have to keep saying what you are.) Irmgard's answer—about
Freddy—lies on the lawn like an old skipping rope, waiting
to catch her up. "Watch me," poor Mrs. Bloodworth said, but
nobody cared, and the cry dissolved. "I like Freddy," Irmgard
said, and was heard, and the statement is there, underfoot.
for if she still likes Freddy, why isn't he here?

Freddy's real name is Alfred Marcel Dufresne. He has
nine sisters and brothers, but doesn't know where they are.
In winter he lives in an orphanage in Montreal. He used to
live there all the year round, but now that he is over seven,
old enough to work, he spends the summer with his uncle,
who has a farm about two miles back from the lake. Freddy
is nearly Irmgard's age, but smaller, lighter on his feet. He
looks a tiny six. When he comes to lunch with Irmgard,

which they have out in the kitchen with Germaine, everything has to be cut on his plate. He has never eaten with anything but a spoon. His chin rests on the edge of the table. When he is eating, you see nothing except his blue eyes, his curly dirty hair, and his hand around the bowl of the spoon. Once, Germaine said calmly, uncritically, "You eat just like a pig," and Freddy repeated in the tone she had used, "*comme un cochon*," as if it were astonishing that someone had, at last, discovered the right words.

Freddy cannot eat, or read, or write, or sing, or swim. He has never seen paints and books, except Irmgard's; he has never been an imaginary person, never played. It was Irmgard who taught him how to swim. He crosses himself before he goes in the water, and looks down at his wet feet, frowning—a worried mosquito—but he does everything she says. The point of their friendship is that she doesn't have to say much. They can read each other's thoughts. When Freddy wants to speak, Irmgard tells him what he wants to say, and Freddy stands there, mute as an animal, grave, nodding, at ease. He does not know the names of flowers, and does not distinguish between the colors green and blue. The apparitions of the Virgin, which are commonplace, take place against a heaven he says is "*vert*."

Now, Bradley has never had a vision, and if he did he wouldn't know what it was. He has no trouble explaining anything. He says, "Well, this is the way it is," and then says. He counts eight beats when he swims, and once saved Irmgard's life—at least he says he did. He says he held on to her braids until someone came by in a boat. No one remembers it but Bradley; it is a myth now, like the *matin du kidnap*. This year, Bradley arrived at the beginning of August. He had spent July in Vermont, where he took tennis lessons and got poison ivy. He was even taller than the year before, and he got down from the train with pink lotion all over his sores and, under his arm, a tennis racket in a press. "What a little stockbroker Bradley is," Irmgard heard her mother say later on; but Mrs. Queen declared that his manners left nothing wanting.

Bradley put all his own things away and set out his toothbrush in a Mickey Mouse glass he travelled with. Then he came down, ready to swim, with his hair water-combed. Irmgard was there, on the gallery, and so was Freddy, hanging on the outside of the railings, his face poked into the morning-glory vines. He thrusts his face between the leaves, and grins, and shows the gaps in his teeth. "How small he is! Do you play with him?" says Bradley, neutrally. Bradley is after information. He needs to know the rules. But if he had been sure about Freddy, if he had seen right away that they could play with Freddy, he would never have asked. And Irmgard replies, "No, I don't," and turns her back. Just so, on her bicycle, coasting downhill, she has lost control and closed her eyes to avoid seeing her own disaster. Dizzily, she says, "No, I don't," and hopes Freddy will disappear. But Freddy continues to hang on, his face thrust among the leaves, until Bradley, quite puzzled now, says, "Well, is he a friend of yours, or what?" and Irmgard again says, "No."

Eventually, that day or the next day, or one day of August, she notices Freddy has gone. Freddy has vanished; but Bradley gives her a poor return. He has the tennis racket, and does nothing except practice against the house. Irmgard has to chase the balls. He practices until his arm is sore, and then he is pleased and says he has tennis arm. Everybody bothers him. The dogs go after the balls and have to be shut up in the garage. "Call the Dogs!" he implores. This is Bradley's voice, over the lake, across the shrinking afternoons. "Please, somebody, call the dogs!"

Freddy is forgotten, but Irmgard thinks she has left something in Montreal. She goes over the things in her personal suitcase. Once, she got up in the night to see if her paintbox was there—if that hadn't been left in Montreal. But the paintbox was there. Something else must be missing. She goes over the list again.

"The fact is," Bradley said, a few days ago, dabbing pink lotion on his poison ivy, "I don't really play with any girls now. So unless you get a brother or something, I probably won't come again." Even with lotion all over his legs he looks splendid. He and Irmgard stand side by side in front of the bathroom looking glass, and admire. She sucks in her cheeks. He peers at his sty. "My mother said you were a stockbroker," Irmgard confides. But Bradley is raised in a different political climate down there in Boston and does not recognize "stockbroker" as a term of abuse. He smiles fatly, and moves his sore tennis arm in a new movement he has now.

During August Freddy no longer existed; she had got in the habit of not seeing him there. But after Bradley's train pulled out, as she sat alone on the dock, kicking the lake, she thought, What'll I do now?, and remembered Freddy. She knows what took place the day she said "No" and, even more, what it meant when she said "Oh, I still like Freddy." But she has forgotten. All she knows now is that when she finds Freddy—in his uncle's muddy farmyard—she understands she hadn't left a paintbox or anything else in Montreal; Freddy was missing, that was all. But Freddy looks old and serious. He hangs his head. He has been forbidden to play with her now, he says. His uncle never wanted him to go there in the first place; it was a waste of time. He only allowed it because they were summer people from Montreal. Wondering where to look, both look at their shoes. Their meeting is made up of Freddy's feet in torn shoes, her sandals, the trampled mud of the yard. Irmgard sees blackberries, not quite ripe. Dumb as Freddy, having lost the power to read his thoughts, she picks blackberries, hard and greenish, and puts them in her mouth.
Freddy's uncle comes out of the foul stable and says something so obscene that the two stand frozen, ashamed—Irmgard, who does not know what the words mean, and Freddy, who does. Then Freddy says he will come with her

for just one swim, and not to Irmgard's dock but to a public beach below the village, where Irmgard is forbidden to go; the water is said to be polluted there.

Germaine has her own way of doing braids. She holds the middle strand of hair in her teeth until she has a good grip on the other two. Then she pulls until Irmgard can feel her scalp lifted from her head. Germaine crosses hands, lets go the middle strand, and is away, breathing heavily. The plaits she makes are glossy and fat, and stay woven in water. She works steadily, breathing on Irmgard's neck.

Mrs. Queen says, "I'll wager you went to see poor Freddy the instant that Bradley was out of sight."

"Mmm."

"Don't 'Mmm' me. I hope he sent you packing."

"We went for a swim."

"I never saw a thing like it. That wretched boy was nothing but a slave to you all summer until Bradley came. It was Freddy do this, come here, go there. That charming English Mrs. Bustard who was here in July remarked the same thing. 'Irmgard is her mother all over again,' Mrs. Bustard said. 'All over again, Mrs. Queen.' "

"*Mrs. Bustard est une espèce de vache,*" says Germaine gently, who cannot understand a word of English.

"Irmgard requires someone with an iron hand. 'A hand of iron,' Mrs. Bustard said."

Irmgard was afraid to tell Freddy, "But we haven't got our bathing suits or any towels." He was silent, and she could no longer read his mind. The sun had gone in. She was uneasy, because she was swimming in a forbidden place, and frightened by the water spiders. There had been other bathers; they had left their candy wrappers behind and a single canvas shoe. The lake was ruffled, brown. She suggested, "It's awfully cold," but Freddy began undressing, and Irmgard, not sure of her ground, began to unbuckle her sandals. They turned their backs, in the usual manner. Irmgard had never seen anybody undressed, and no one had ever seen her, except Germaine. Her back to Freddy, she pulled off her cotton dress, but kept on her bloomers. When she turned again, Freddy was naked. It was not a mistake; she had not turned around too soon. He stood composedly, with one hand on his skinny ribs. She said only, "The water's dirty here," and again, "It's cold." There were tin cans in the lake, half sunk in mud, and the water spiders. When they came out, Irmgard stood goosefleshed, blue-lipped. Freddy had not said a word. Trembling, wet, they put on their clothes. Irmgard felt water running into her shoes. She said miserably, "I think my mother wants me now," and edged one foot behind the other, and turned, and went away. There was nothing they could say, and nothing they could play any longer. He had discovered that he could live without her. None of the old games would do.

Germaine knows. This is what Germaine said yesterday afternoon; she was simple and calm, and said, "*Oui, c'est comme ça. C'est bien malheureux. Tu sais, ma p'tite fille, je crois qu'un homme, c'est une déformation.*"

Irmgard leans against Germaine. They seem to be consoling each other, because of what they both know. Mrs. Queen says, "Freddy goes back to an orphan asylum. I knew from the beginning the way it would end. It was not a kindness, allowing him to come here. It was no kindness at all." She would say more, but they have come down and want their breakfast. After keeping her up all night with noise, they want their breakfast now.

Mrs. Bloodworth looks distressed and unwashed. Her friend has asked for beer instead of coffee. Pleasure followed by gloom is a regular pattern here. But no matter how they feel, Irmgard's parents get up and come down for breakfast, and they judge their guests by the way they behave not in pleasure but in remorse. The man who has asked for beer as medicine and not for enjoyment, and who described the condition of his stomach and the roots of his hair, will never be invited again. Irmgard stands by her mother's chair; for the mother is the mirror, and everything is reflected or darkened, given life or dismissed, in the picture her mother returns. The lake, the house, the summer, the reason for doing one thing instead of another are reflected here, explained, clarified. If the mirror breaks, everything will break, too.

They are talking quietly at the breakfast table. The day began in fine shape, but now it is going to be cloudy again. They think they will all go to Montreal. It is nearly Labor Day. The pity of parties is that they end.

"Are you sad, too, now that your little boy friend has left you?" says Mrs. Bloodworth, fixing Irmgard with her still-sleeping eyes. She means Bradley; she thought he and Irmgard were perfectly sweet.

Now, this is just the way they don't like Irmgard spoken to, and Irmgard knows they will not invite Mrs. Bloodworth again, either. They weigh and measure and sift everything people say, and Irmgard's father looks cold and bored, and her mother gives a waking tiger's look his way, smiles. They act together, and read each other's thoughts—just as Freddy and Irmgard did. But, large, and old, and powerful, they have greater powers: they see through walls, and hear whispered conversations miles away. Irmgard's father looks cold, and Irmgard, without knowing it, imitates his look.

"Bradley is Irmgard's cousin," her mother says.

Now Irmgard, who cannot remember anything, who looked for a paintbox when Freddy had gone, who doesn't remember that she was kidnapped and that Bradley once saved her life—now Irmgard remembers something. It seems that Freddy was sent on an errand. He went off down the sidewalk, which was heaving, cracked, edged with ribbon grass; and when he came to a certain place he was no longer there. Something was waiting for him there, and when they came looking for him, only Irmgard knew that whatever had been waiting for Freddy was the disaster, the worst thing. Irmgard's mother said, "Imagine sending a child near the woods at this time of day!" Sure enough, there were trees nearby. And only Irmgard knew that whatever had been waiting for Freddy had come out of the woods. It was the worst thing; and it could not be helped. But she does not know exactly what it was. And then, was it Freddy? It might have been Bradley, or even herself.

Naturally, no child should go near a strange forest. There are chances of getting lost. There is the witch who changes children into birds.

Irmgard grows red in the face and says loudly, "I remember my dream. Freddy went on a message and got lost."

"Oh, no dreams at breakfast, please," her father says.

"Nothing is as dreary as a dream," her mother says, agreeing. "I think we might make a rule on that: no dreams at breakfast. Otherwise it gets to be a habit."

Her father cheers up. Nothing cheers them up so fast as a new rule, for when it comes to making rules, they are as bad as children. You should see them at croquet.

By the River

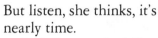

But listen, she thinks, it's nearly time.

And flutters, leaf-like, at the thought. The train will rumble down the valley, stop at the little shack to discharge Styan, and move on. This will happen in half an hour and she has a mile still to walk.

Crystal Styan walking through the woods, through bush, is not pretty. She knows that she is not even a little pretty, though her face is small enough, and pale, and her eyes are not too narrow. She wears a yellow wool sweater and a long cotton skirt and boots. Her hair, tied back so the branches will not catch in it, hangs straight and almost colourless down her back. Some day, she expects, there will be a baby to play with her hair and hide in it like someone behind a waterfall.

She has left the log cabin, which sits on the edge of the river in a stand of birch, and now she follows the river bank upstream. A mile ahead, far around the bend out of sight, the railroad tracks pass along the rim of their land and a small station is built there just for them, for her and Jim Styan. It is

JACK
HODGINS

47

their only way in to town, which is ten miles away and not much of a town anyway when you get there. A few stores, a tilted old hotel, a movie theatre.

Likely, Styan would have been to a movie last night. He would have stayed the night in the hotel, but first (after he had seen the lawyer and bought the few things she'd asked him for) he would pay his money and sit in the back row of the theatre and laugh loudly all the way through the movie. He always laughs at everything, even if it isn't funny, because those figures on the screen make him think of people he has known; and the thought of them exposed like this for just anyone to see embarrasses him a little and makes him want to create a lot of noise so people will know he isn't a bit like that himself.

She smiles. The first time they went to a movie together she slouched as far down in the seat as she could so no one could see she was there or had anything to do with Jim Styan.

The river flows past her almost silently. It has moved only a hundred miles from its source and has another thousand miles to go before it reaches the ocean, but already it is wide enough and fast. Right here she has more than once seen a moose wade out and then swim across to the other side and disappear into the cedar swamps. She knows something, has heard somewhere that farther downstream, miles and miles behind her, an Indian band once thought this river a hungry monster that liked to gobble up their people. They say that Coyote their god-hero dived in and subdued the monster and made it promise never to swallow people again. She once thought she'd like to study that kind of thing at a university or somewhere, if Jim Styan hadn't told her grade ten was good enough for anyone and a life on the road was more exciting.

What road? she wonders. There isn't a road within ten miles. They sold the rickety old blue pickup the same day they moved onto this place. The railroad was going to be all they'd need. There wasn't any place they cared to go that the train, even this old-fashioned milk-run outfit, couldn't take them easily and cheaply enough.

But listen, she thinks, it's nearly time.

The trail she is following swings inland to climb a small bluff and for a while she is engulfed by trees. Cedar and fir are dark and thick and damp. The green new growth on the scrub bushes has nearly filled in the narrow trail. She holds her skirt up a little so it won't be caught or ripped, then runs and nearly slides down the hill again to the river's bank. She can see in every direction for miles and there isn't a thing in sight which has anything to do with man.

"Who needs them?" Styan said, long ago.

It was with that kind of question—questions that implied an answer so obvious only a fool would think to doubt—that he talked her first out of the classroom and then right off the island of her birth and finally up here into the mountains with the river and the moose and the railroad. It was as if he had transported her in his falling-apart pickup not only across the province about as far as it was possible to go, but also backwards in time, perhaps as far as her grandmother's youth or even farther. She washes their coarse clothing in the river and depends on the whims of the seasons for her food.

"Look!" he shouted when they stood first in the clearing above the cabin. "It's as if we're the very first ones. You and me."

They swam in the cold river that day and even then she thought of Coyote and the monster, but he took her inside the cabin and they made love on the fir-bough bed that was to be theirs for the next five years. "We don't need any of them," he sang. He flopped over on his back and shouted up into the rafters. "We'll farm it! We'll make it go. We'll make our own world!" Naked, he was as thin and pale as a celery stalk.

When they moved in he let his moustache grow long and droopy like someone in an old, brown photograph. He wore overalls which were far too big for him and started walking around as if there were a movie camera somewhere in the trees and he was being paid to act like a hillbilly instead of the city-bred boy he really was. He stuck a limp felt hat on the top of his head like someone's uncle Hiram and bought chickens.

"It's a start," he said.

"Six chickens?" She counted again to be sure. "We don't even have a shed for them."

He stood with his feet wide apart and looked at her as if she were stupid. "They'll lay their eggs in the grass."

"That should be fun," she said. "A hundred and sixty acres is a good-size pen."

"It's a start. Next spring we'll buy a cow. Who needs more?"

Yes who? They survived their first winter here, though the chickens weren't so lucky. The hens got lice and started pecking at each other. By the time Styan got around to riding in to town for something to kill the lice a few had pecked right through the skin and exposed the innards. When he came back from town they had all frozen to death in the yard.

At home, back on her father's farm in the blue mountains of the island, nothing had ever frozen to death. Her father had cared for things. She had never seen anything go so wrong there, or anyone have to suffer.

She walks carefully now, for the trail is on the very edge of the river bank and is spongy and broken away in places. The water, clear and shallow here, back-eddies into little bays where cattail and bracken grow and where water-skeeters walk on their own reflection. A beer bottle glitters where someone, perhaps a guide on the river, has thrown it—wedged between stones as if it has been there as long as they have. She keeps her face turned to the river, away from the acres and acres of forest which are theirs.

Listen, it's nearly time, she thinks. And knows that soon, from far up the river valley, she will be able to hear the throbbing of the train, coming near.

She imagines his face at the window. He is the only passenger in the coach and sits backwards, watching the land slip by, grinning in expectation or memory or both. He tells a joke to old Bill Cobb the conductor but even in his laughter does not turn his eyes from outside the train. One spot on his forehead is white where it presses against the glass. His fingers run over and over the long drooping ends of his moustache. He is wearing his hat.

Hurry, hurry, she thinks. To the train, to her feet, to him.

She wants to tell him about the skunk she spotted yesterday. She wants to tell him about the stove, which smokes too much and needs some kind of clean-out. She wants to tell him about her dream; how she dreamed he was trying to go into the river and how she pulled and hauled on his feet but he wouldn't come out. He will laugh and laugh at her when she tells him, and his laughter will make it all right and not so frightening, so that maybe she will be able to laugh at it too.

She has rounded the curve in the river and glances back, way back, at the cabin. It is dark and solid, not far from the bank. Behind the poplars the cleared fields are yellowing with the coming of fall but now in all that place there isn't a thing alive, unless she wants to count trees and insects. No people. No animals. It is scarcely different from her very first look at it. In five years their dream of livestock has been shelved again and again.

Once there was a cow. A sway-backed old Jersey.

"This time I've done it right," he said. "Just look at this prize."

And stepped down off the train to show off his cow, a wide-eyed beauty that looked at her through a window of the passenger coach.

"Maybe so, but you'll need a miracle, too, to get that thing down out of there."

A minor detail to him, who scooped her up and swung her around and kissed her hard, all in front of the old conductor and the engineer who didn't even bother to turn away.

"Farmers at last!" he shouted. "You can't have a farm without a cow. You can't have a baby without a cow."

She put her head inside the coach, looked square into the big brown eyes, glanced at the sawed-off horns. "Found you somewhere, I guess," she said to the cow. "Turned out of someone's herd for being too old or senile or dried up."

"An auction sale," he said, and slapped one hand on the window glass. "I was the only one there who was desperate. But I punched her bag and pulled her tits; she'll do. There may even be a calf or two left in her sway-backed old soul."

"Come on, bossy," she said. "This is no place for you."

But the cow had other ideas. It backed into a corner of the coach and shook its lowered head. Its eyes, steady and dull, never left Crystal Styan.

"You're home," Styan said. "Sorry there's no crowd here or a band playing music, but step down anyway and let's get started."

"She's not impressed," she said. "She don't see any barn waiting out there either, not to mention hay or feed of any kind. She's smart enough to know a train coach is at least a roof over her head."

The four of them climbed over the seats to get behind her and pushed her all the way down the aisle. Then, when they had shoved her down the steps, she fell on her knees on the gravel and let out a long unhappy bellow. She looked around, bellowed again, then stood up and high-tailed it down the tracks. Before Styan even thought to go after her she swung right and headed into bush.

Styan disappeared into the bush, too, hollering, and after a while the train moved on to keep its schedule. She went back down the trail and waited in the cabin until nearly dark. When she went outside again she found him on the river bank, his feet in the water, his head resting against a birch trunk.

"What the hell," he said, and shook his head and didn't look at her.

"Maybe she'll come back," she said.

"A bear'll get her before then, or a cougar. There's no hope of that."

She put a hand on his shoulder but he shook it off. He'd dragged her from place to place right up this river from its mouth, looking and looking for his dream, never satisfied until he saw this piece of land. For that dream and for him she had suffered.

She smiles, though, at the memory. Because even then he was able to bounce back, resume the dream, start building new plans. She smiles, too, because she knows there will be a surprise today; there has always been a surprise. When it wasn't a cow it was a bouquet of flowers or something else. She goes through a long list in her mind of what it may be, but knows it will be none of them. Not once in her life has anything been exactly the way she imagined it. Just so much as foreseeing something was a guarantee it wouldn't happen, at least not in the exact same way.

"Hey you, Styan!" she suddenly calls out. "Hey you, Jim Styan. Where are you?" And laughs, because the noise she makes can't possibly make any difference to the world, except for a few wild animals that might be alarmed.

She laughs again, and slaps one hand against her thigh, and shakes her head. Just give her—how many minutes now?—and she won't be alone. These woods will shudder with his laughter, his shouting, his joy. That train, that kinky little train will drop her husband off and then pass on like a stay-stitch thread pulled from a seam.

"Hey you, Styan! What you brought this time? A gold brooch? An old nanny goat?"

The river runs past silently and she imagines that it is only shoulders she is seeing, that monster heads have ducked down to glide by but are watching her from eyes grey as stone. She wants to scream out "Hide, you crummy cheat, my Coyote's coming home!" but is afraid to tempt even something that she does not believe in. And anyway she senses—far off—the beat of the little train coming down the valley from the town.

And when it comes into sight she is there, on the platform in front of the little sagging shed, watching. She stands
tilted far out over the tracks to see, but never dares—even
when it is so far away—to step down onto the ties for a
better look.

The boards beneath her feet are rotting and broken. Long
stems of grass have grown up through the cracks and brush
against her legs. A squirrel runs down the slope of the shed's
roof and yatters at her until she turns and lifts her hand to
frighten it into silence.

She talks to herself, sings almost to the engine's beat—
"Here he comes, here he comes"—and has her smile already
as wide as it can be. She smiles into the side of the locomotive sliding past and the freight car sliding past and keeps on
smiling even after the coach has stopped in front of her and
it is obvious that Jim Styan is not on board.

Unless of course he is hiding under one of the seats, ready
to leap up, one more surprise.

But old Bill Cobb the conductor backs down the steps,
dragging a gunny sack out after him. "H'lo there, Crystal,"
he says. "He ain't aboard today either, I'm afraid." He works
the gunny sack out onto the middle of the platform. "Herbie
Stark sent this, it's potatoes mostly, and cabbages he was
going to throw out of his store."

She takes the tiniest peek inside the sack and yes, there
are potatoes there and some cabbages with soft brown
leaves.

The engineer steps down out of his locomotive and comes
along the side of the train rolling a cigarette. "Nice day
again," he says with barely a glance at the sky. "You makin'
out all right?"

"Hold it," the conductor says, as if he expects the train to
move off by itself. "There's more." He climbs back into the
passenger car and drags out a cardboard box heaped with
groceries. "The church ladies said to drop this off," he says.
"They told me make sure you get every piece of it, but I don't

know how you'll ever get it down to the house through all that bush."

"She'll manage," the engineer says. He holds a lighted match under the ragged end of his cigarette until the loose tobacco blazes up. "She's been doing it—how long now?— must be six months."

The conductor pushes the cardboard box over against the sack of potatoes and stands back to wipe the sweat off his face. He glances at the engineer and they both smile a little and turn away. "Well," the engineer says, and heads back down the tracks and up into his locomotive.

The conductor tips his hat, says "Sorry," and climbs back into the empty passenger car. The train releases a long hiss and then moves slowly past her and down the tracks into the deep bush. She stands on the platform and looks after it a long while, as if a giant hand is pulling, slowly, a stay-stitching thread out of a fuzzy green cloth.

After the Sirens

They heard the sirens first about four forty-five in the morning. It was still dark and cold outside and they were sound asleep. They heard the noise first in their dreams and, waking, understood it to be real.

"What is it?" she asked him sleepily, rolling over in their warm bed. "Is there a fire?"

"I don't know," he said. The sirens were very loud. "I've never heard anything like that before."

"It's some kind of siren," she said, "downtown. It woke me up."

"Go back to sleep!" he said. "It can't be anything."

"No," she said, "I'm frightened. I wonder what it is. I wonder if the baby has enough covers." The wailing was still going on. "It couldn't be an air-raid warning, could it?"

"Of course not," he said reassuringly, but she could hear the indecision in his voice.

"Why don't you turn on the radio," she said, "just to see? Just to make sure. I'll go and see if the baby's covered up." They walked down the hall in their

HUGH
HOOD

pajamas. He went into the kitchen, turned on the radio and waited for it to warm up. There was nothing but static and hum.

"What's that station?" he called to her. "Conrad, or something like that."

"That's 640 on the dial," she said, from the baby's room. He twisted the dial and suddenly the radio screamed at him, frightening him badly.

"This is not an exercise. This is not an exercise. This is not an exercise," the radio blared. *"This is an air-raid warning. This is an air-raid warning. We will be attacked in fifteen minutes. We will be attacked in fifteen minutes. This is not an exercise."* He recognized the voice of a local announcer who did an hour of breakfast music daily. He had never heard the man talk like that before. He ran into the baby's room while the radio shrieked behind him: *"We will be attacked in fifteen minutes. Correction. Correction. In fourteen minutes. In fourteen minutes. We will be attacked in fourteen minutes. This is not an exercise."*

"Look," he said, "don't ask me any questions, please, just do exactly what I tell you and don't waste any time." She stared at him with her mouth open. "Listen," he said, "and do exactly as I say. They say this is an air-raid and we'd better believe them." She looked frightened nearly out of her wits. "I'll look after you," he said; "just get dressed as fast as you can. Put on as many layers of wool as you can. Got that?"

She nodded speechlessly.

"Put on your woollen topcoat and your fur coat over that. Get as many scarves as you can find. We'll wrap our faces and hands. When you're dressed, dress the baby the same way. We have a chance, if you do as I say without wasting time." She ran off up the hall to the coat closet and he could hear her pulling things about.

"This will be an attack with nuclear weapons. You have thirteen minutes to take cover," screamed the radio. He looked at his watch and hurried to the kitchen and pulled a

cardboard carton from under the sink. He threw two can openers into it and all the canned goods he could see. There were three loaves of bread in the breadbox and he crammed them into the carton. He took everything that was wrapped and solid in the refrigerator and crushed it in. When the carton was full he took a bucket which usually held a garbage bag, rinsed it hastily, and filled it with water. There was a plastic bottle in the refrigerator. He poured the tomato juice out of it and rinsed it and filled it with water.

"*This will be a nuclear attack.*" The disc jockey's voice was cracking with hysteria. "*You have nine minutes, nine minutes, to take cover. Nine minutes.*" He ran into the dark hall and bumped into his wife who was swaddled like a bear.

"Go and dress the baby," he said. "We're going to make it, we've just got time. I'll go and get dressed." She was crying, but there was no time for comfort. In the bedroom he forced himself into his trousers, a second pair of trousers, two shirts and two sweaters. He put on the heaviest, loosest jacket he owned, a topcoat, and finally his overcoat. This took him just under five minutes. When he rejoined his wife in the living room, she had the baby swaddled in her arms, still asleep.

"Go to the back room in the cellar, where your steamer trunk is," he said, "and take this." He gave her a flashlight which they kept in their bedroom. When she hesitated he said roughly, "Go on, get going."

"Aren't you coming?"

"Of course I'm coming," he said. He turned the radio up as far as it would go and noted carefully what the man said. "*This will be a nuclear attack. The target will probably be the aircraft company. You have three minutes to take cover.*" He picked up the carton and balanced the bottle of water on it. With the other hand he carried the bucket. Leaving the kitchen door wide open, he went to the cellar, passed through the dark furnace room, and joined his wife.

"Put out the flashlight," he said. "We'll have to save it. We have a minute or two, so listen to me." They could hear the radio upstairs. *"Two minutes,"* it screamed.

"Lie down in the corner of the west and north walls," he said quickly. "The blast should come from the north if they hit the target, and the house will blow down and fall to the south. Lie on top of the baby and I'll lie on top of you!"

She cuddled the sleeping infant in her arms. "We're going to die right now," she said, as she held the baby closer to her.

"No, we aren't," he said, "we have a chance. Wrap the scarves around your face and the baby's, and lie down." She handed him a plaid woollen scarf and he tied it around his face so that only his eyes showed. He placed the water and food in a corner and then lay down on top of his wife, spreading his arms and legs as much as possible, to cover and protect her.

"Twenty seconds," shrieked the radio. *"Eighteen seconds. Fifteen."*

He looked at his watch as he fell. "Ten seconds," he said aloud. "It's five o'clock. They won't waste a megaton bomb on us. They'll save it for New York." They heard the radio crackle into silence and they hung onto each other, keeping their eyes closed tightly.

Instantaneously the cellar room lit up with a kind of glow they had never seen before, the earthen floor began to rock and heave, and the absolutely unearthly sound began. There was no way of telling how far off it was, the explosion. The sound seemed to be inside them, in their bowels; the very air itself was shattered and blown away in the dreadful sound that went on and on and on.

They held their heads down, hers pushed into the dirt, shielding the baby's scalp, his face crushed into her hair, nothing of their skin exposed to the glow, and the sound went on and on, pulsing curiously, louder than anything they had ever imagined, louder than deafening, quaking in their eardrums, louder and louder until it seemed that what had exploded was there in the room on top of them in a blend of smashed, torn air, cries of the instantly dead, fall of steel, timber, and brick, crash of masonry and glass—they couldn't sort any of it out—all were there, all imaginable noises of destruction synthesized. It was like absolutely nothing they had ever heard before and it so filled their skulls, pushing outward from the brainpan, that they could not divide it into its parts. All that they could understand, if they understood anything, was that this was the ultimate catastrophe, and that they were still recording it, expecting any second to be crushed into blackness, but as long as they were recording it they were still living. They felt, but did not think, this. They only understood it instinctively and held on tighter to each other, waiting for the smash, the crush, the black.

But it became lighter and lighter, the glow in the cellar room, waxing and intensifying itself. It had no color that they recognized through their tightly-shut eyelids. It might have been called green, but it was not green, nor any neighbor of green. Like the noise, it was a dreadful compound of ultimately destructive fire, blast, terrible energy released from a bursting sun, like the birth of the solar system. Incandescence beyond an infinite number of lights swirled around them.

The worst was the nauseous rocking to and fro of the very earth beneath them, worse than an earthquake, which might have seemed reducible to human dimensions, those of some disaster witnessed in the movies or on television. But this was no gaping, opening seam in the earth, but a threatened total destruction of the earth itself, right to its core, a pulverization of the world. They tried like animals to scrabble closer and closer in under the north cellar wall even as they expected it to fall on them. They kept their heads down, waiting for death to take them as it had taken their friends, neighbors, fellow workers, policemen, firemen, soldiers; and the dreadful time passed and still they did not die in the catastrophe. And they began to sense obscurely that the

longer they were left uncrushed, the better grew their chances of survival. And pitifully slowly their feelings began to
resume their customary segmented play amongst themselves, while the event was still unfolding. They could not
help doing the characteristic, the human thing, the beginning to think and struggle to live.

Through their shut eyelids the light began to seem less
incandescent, more recognizably a color familiar to human
beings and less terrifying because it might be called a hue of
green instead of no-color-at-all. It became green, still glow-
ing and illuminating the cellar like daylight, but anyway
green, nameable as such and therefore familiar and less
dreadful. The light grew more and more darkly green in an
insane harmony with the rocking and the sound.

As the rocking slowed, as they huddled closer and closer in
under the north foundation, a split in the cellar wall showed
itself almost in front of their hidden faces, and yet the wall
stood and did not come in on top of them. It held and,
holding, gave them more chance for survival although they
didn't know it. The earth's upheaval slowed and sank back
and no gaps appeared in the earth under them, no crevasse
to swallow them up under the alteration of the earth's crust.
And in time the rocking stopped and the floor of their world
was still, but they would not move, afraid to move a limb for
fear of being caught in the earth's mouth.

The noise continued, but began to distinguish itself in
parts, and the worst basic element attenuated itself; that
terrible crash apart of the atmosphere under the bomb had
stopped by now, the atmosphere had parted to admit the
ball of radioactivity, had been blown hundreds of miles in
every direction and had rushed back to regain its place,
disputing that place with the ball of radioactivity, so that
there grew up a thousand-mile vortex of cyclonic winds
around the hub of the displacement. The cyclone was almost
comforting, sounding, whistling, in whatever stood upright,
not trees certainly, but tangled steel beams and odd bits of

masonry. The sound of these winds came to them in the cellar. Soon they were able to name sounds, and distinguish them from others which they heard, mainly sounds of fire— no sounds of the dying, no human cries at all, no sounds of life. Only the fires and cyclonic winds.

Now they could feel, and hear enough to shout to each other over the fire and wind.

The man tried to stir, to ease his wife's position. He could move his torso so far as the waist or perhaps the hips. Below that, although he was in no pain and not paralyzed, he was immobilized by a heavy weight. He could feel his legs and feet; they were sound and unhurt, but he could not move them. He waited, lying there trying to sort things out, until some sort of ordered thought and some communication was possible, when the noise should lessen sufficiently. He could hear his wife shouting something into the dirt in front of her face and he tried to make it out.

"She slept through it," he heard, "she slept through it," and he couldn't believe it, although it was true. The baby lived and recollected none of the horror.

"She slept through it," screamed the wife idiotically, "she's still asleep." It couldn't be true, he thought, it was impossible, but there was no way to check her statement until they could move about. The baby must have been three feet below the blast and the glow, shielded by a two-and-a-half-foot wall of flesh, his and his wife's, and the additional thickness of layers of woollen clothing. She should certainly have survived, if they had, but how could she have slept through the noise, the awful light, and the rocking? He listened and waited, keeping his head down and his face covered.

Supposing that they had survived the initial blast, as seemed to be the case; there was still the fallout to consider. The likelihood, he thought (he was beginning to be able to think) was that they were already being eaten up by radiation and would soon die of monstrous cancers, or plain, simple leukemia, or rottenness of the cortex. It was miraculous that they had lived through the first shock; they could hardly hope that their luck would hold through the later dangers. He thought that the baby might not have been infected so far, shielded as she was, as he began to wonder how she might be helped to evade death from radiation in the next few days. Let her live a week, he thought, and she may go on living into the next generation, if there is one.

Nothing would be the same in the next generation; there would be few people and fewer laws, the national boundaries would have perished—there would be a new world to invent. Somehow the child must be preserved for that, even if their own lives were to be forfeited immediately. He felt perfectly healthy so far, untouched by any creeping sickness as he lay there, forcing himself and the lives beneath him deeper into their burrow. He began to make plans; there was nothing else for him to do just then.

The noise of the winds had become regular now and the green glow had subsided; the earth was still and they were still together and in the same place, in their cellar, in their home. He thought of his books, his checkbook, his phonograph records, his wife's household appliances. They were gone, of course, which didn't matter. What mattered was that the way they had lived was gone, the whole texture of their habits. The city would be totally uninhabitable. If they were to survive longer, they must get out of the city at once. They would have to decide immediately when they should try to leave the city, and they must keep themselves alive until that time.

"What time is it?" gasped his wife from below him in a tone pitched in almost her normal voice. He was relieved to hear her speak in the commonplace, familiar tone; he had been afraid that hysteria and shock would destroy their personalities all at once. So far they had held together. Later on, when the loss of their whole world sank in, when they appreciated the full extent of their losses, they would run the risk of insanity or, at least, extreme neurotic disturbance. But right now they could converse, calculate, and wait for the threat of madness to appear days, or years, later.

He looked at his watch. "Eight-thirty," he said. Everything had ended in three-and-a-half hours. "Are you all right?" he asked.

"I think so," she said, "I don't feel any pain and the baby's fine. She's warm and she doesn't seem frightened."

He tried to move his legs and was relieved to see that they answered the nervous impulse. He lifted his head fearfully and twisted it around to see behind him. His legs were buried under a pile of loose brick and rubble which grew smaller toward his thighs; his torso was quite uncovered. "I'm all right," he said, beginning to work his legs free; they were undoubtedly badly bruised, but they didn't seem to be crushed or broken; at the worst he might have torn muscles or a bad sprain. He had to be very careful, he reasoned, as he worked at his legs. He might dislodge something and bring the remnant of the house down around them. Very, very slowly he lifted his torso by doing a push-up with his arms. His wife slid out from underneath, pushing the baby in front of her. When she was free she laid the child gently to one side, whispering to her and promising her food. She crawled around to her husband's side and began to push the bricks off his legs.

"Be careful," he whispered. "Take them as they come. Don't be in too much of a hurry."

She nodded, picking out the bricks gingerly, but as fast as she could. Soon he was able to roll over on his back and sit up. By a quarter to ten he was free and they took time to eat and drink. The three of them sat together in a cramped, narrow space under the cellar beams, perhaps six feet high and six or seven feet square. They were getting air from somewhere although it might be deadly air, and there was no smell of gas. He had been afraid that they might be suffocated in their shelter.

"Do you suppose the food's contaminated?" she asked.

"What if it is?" he said. "So are we, just as much as the food. There's nothing to do but risk it. Only be careful what you give the baby."

"How can I tell?"

"I don't know," he said. "Say a prayer and trust in God." He found the flashlight, which had rolled into a corner, and tried it. It worked very well.

"What are we going to do? We can't stay here."

"I don't even know for sure that we can get out," he said, "but we'll try. There should be a window just above us that leads to a crawl-space under the patio. That's one of the reasons why I told you to come here. In any case we'd be wise to stay here for a few hours until the very worst of the fallout is down."

"What'll we do when we get out?"

"Try to get out of town. Get our outer clothes off, get them all off for that matter, and scrub ourselves with water. Maybe we can get to the river."

"Why don't you try the window right now so we can tell whether we can get out?"

"I will as soon as I've finished eating and had a rest. My legs are very sore."

He could hear her voice soften. "Take your time," she said.

When he felt rested, he stood up. He could almost stand erect and with the flashlight was able to find the window quickly. It was level with his face. He piled loose bricks against the wall below it and climbed up on them until the window was level with his chest. Knocking out the screen with the butt of the flashlight, he put his head through and then flashed the light around; there were no obstructions that he could see, and he couldn't smell anything noxious. The patio, being a flat, level space, had evidently been swept clean by the blast without being flattened. They could crawl out of the cellar under the patio, he realized, and then kick a hole in the lath and stucco which skirted it.

He stepped down from the pile of brick and told his wife that they would be able to get out whenever they wished, that the crawl space was clear.

"What time is it?"

"Half-past twelve."

"Should we try it now?"

"I think so," he said. "At first I thought we ought to stay here for a day or two, but now I think we ought to try and get out from under the fallout. We may have to walk a couple of hundred miles."

"We can do it," she said and he felt glad. She had always been able to look unpleasant issues in the face.

He helped her through the cellar window and handed up the baby, who clucked and chuckled when he spoke to her. He pushed the carton of food and the bucket of water after them. Then he climbed up and they inched forward under the patio.

"I hear a motor," said his wife suddenly.

He listened and heard it too.

"Looking for survivors," he said eagerly. "Probably the Army or Civil Defense. Come on."

He swung himself around on his hips and back and kicked out with both feet at the lath and stucco. Three or four kicks did it. His wife went first, inching the baby through the hole. He crawled after her into the daylight; it looked like any other day except that the city was leveled. The sky and the light were the same; everything else was gone. They sat up, muddy, scratched, nervously exhausted, in a ruined flower bed. Not fifty feet away stood an olive-drab truck, the motor running loudly. Men shouted to them.

"Come on, you!" shouted the men in the truck. "Get going!" They stood and ran raggedly to the cab, she holding the child and he their remaining food and water. In the cab was a canvas-sheeted, goggled driver, peering at them through huge eyes. "Get in the back," he ordered. "We've got to get out right away. Too hot." They climbed into the truck and it began to move instantly.

"Army Survival Unit," said a goggled and hooded man in the back of the truck. "Throw away that food and water; it's dangerous. Get your outer clothing off quick. Throw it out!" They obeyed him without thinking, stripping off their loose outer clothes and dropping them out of the truck.

"You're the only ones we've found in a hundred city blocks," said the soldier. "Did you know the war's over? There's a truce."

"Who won?"

"Over in half an hour," he said, "and nobody won."

"What are you going to do with us?"

"Drop you at a check-out point forty miles from here. Give you the scrub-down treatment, wash off the fallout. Medical check for radiation sickness. Clean clothes. Then we send you on your way to a refugee station."

"How many died?"

"Everybody in the area. Almost no exceptions. You're a statistic, that's what you are. Must have been a fluke of the blast."

"Will we live?"

"Sure you will. You're living now, aren't you?"

"I guess so," he said.

"Sure you'll live! Maybe not too long. But everybody else is dead! And you'll be taken care of." He fell silent.

They looked at each other, determined to live as long as they could. The wife cuddled the child close against her thin silk blouse. For a long time they jolted along over rocks and broken pavement without speaking. When the pavement smoothed out the husband knew that they must be out of the disaster area. In a few more minutes they were out of immediate danger; they had reached the checkout point. It was a quarter to three in the afternoon.

"Out you get," said the soldier. "We've got to go back." They climbed out of the truck and he handed down the baby. "You're all right now," he said. "Good luck."

"Good-bye," they said.

The truck turned about and drove away and they turned silently, hand in hand, and walked toward the medical tents. They were the seventh, eight, and ninth living persons to be brought there after the sirens.

The Voices of Adamo

His mother was warmth and coolness. Warmth at daybreak when the children, sleeping like clustered toads in the dank hut corner, wakened hungry and straggled outside to find always that she was up before them and had the cocoyam cooking in the black iron pot. Warmth when the rain came at night, when the thunder howled its unknowable threats and the children shivered with chill and fear. Coolness in the heat of the day, when Adamo's legs were tired from trying to keep up with the older ones, cool shadow in her arms and her vast body bending over him. Before Adamo knew anything he knew this, his mother's sun and shade.

She gathered firewood and the children beside her gleaned twigs. When she went to hoe the cassava patch, Adamo and the others learned to walk through the fern-thick forest lightly, slipping around the thorns that would tear flesh, placing their feet so. She showed her young how to remain

MARGARET
LAURENCE

motionless in the snake's presence—not the tight contain-
ment of panic, for a brittle branch may snap, but a silent
infolding of muscles like a leaf bud.

Afternoons, the girls stayed with their mother to tend the
fire and pound the dried yam in the big wooden bowls. But
Adamo and his brothers swam in the tepid slime-edged river
or climbed the nut palms at the edge of the sacred grove or
watched Ofei the blacksmith at his smoky forge turning a
new machete.

The days flowed slowly as the river, and when Adamo was
no longer a young child, his father taught him what he must
know to wrench existence from the forest and yet not turn
to vengeance the spirit that animated all things—the tree he
felled, the plant he harvested, the antelope whose life he
must take to feed his own. The forbidden acts and words
were many, and the words and acts of appeasement were
many, but Adamo dared not forget, for an offender en-
dangered not only himself but the entire village, and that
was the worst any person could do.

"A man is a leaf," Adamo's father would say in his stern
and quiet voice. "The leaf grows for a while, then falls, but
the tree lives for ever. One leaf is nothing. The tree is all."

Regularly, meticulously, the offerings of mashed yam or
eggs were made to the gods of river and forest. The invoca-
tions entered into Adamo, for he would speak one day with
the same calm voice as his father's.

"Here is food from our hands. Receive this food and eat.
Stand behind us with a good standing. Let the women bear
children. Let the yams grow. Let nothing evil befall."

Adamo's father was strong. He knew always what to do.
His own father and his mother had been dead for many
years, but they were with him. He heard their guiding voices
in the night wind. He poured palm wine on their graves, and
they drank. They had never left him. When Adamo's mother
and father died, they would not leave him, either.

Sometimes it was not enough, and the feared thing happened. Adamo's youngest sister was taken by the crocodile. When the mother turned at the cry, she saw only the blood swirling like flames on the water. Adamo's brother Kwadwo died of a fever, although his wrists and forehead had been bound with costly medicinal charms from Yao the fetish priest. These deaths they mourned each with a terrible stone in the heart, wondering who had been the one to cause by some offence such retribution.

So Adamo learned fear, but the fears were not the greater part. As long as the laws were kept, the palms and the dark river and the red earth were to Adamo like his own brothers, who would not forsake him.

When Adamo was fifteen, a sickness struck the village. That it was smallpox meant nothing to him. But because he was the youngest of her four remaining sons, his mother was determined that Adamo must go until the sickness was over. She had a friend in a village not so far away. He did not want to go, but when his father said it would be best, Adamo went.

His mother's friend welcomed him into her family. Adamo stayed on and on, at first unquestioning, then with a faint anxiety, finally desperate to return home. But always the answer was the same.

"We have heard nothing, Adamo. You are doing good work here—stay."

Sunrise gave way to mid-day, and mid-day to sunset. Adamo had no notion that he had lived in this other village for a year. But one day when he went to wash himself in the river, he heard his mother's voice. The voice, gentle and persistent, spoke inside his head.

Adamo—where are you? Adamo—where are we?

That night he put his machete and his cloth and the knife which his father had given him into a bundle and walked out, without a word, along the bush trail that led back to his village.

The thorn bushes and liana vines by day were green nets

that could snare only an unwatchful traveller, but at night they changed, became formless and yet solid, a heaviness of dark before the eyes. Anything a pace away seemed nonexistent, as though the world stopped where the foot fell. Adamo had no light. A man needs a light, not so much against the outer darkness, as to be sure that he himself is really there. With his bare feet, Adamo could feel the path. He stumbled over tree roots, slipped on the decay of last year's growth, grasped at branches and found his hands held ferns, insubstantial as spider-webs. But although he feared, he never doubted that he would reach his village, for his mother's voice drew him on.

Adamo—where are you? Adamo—where are we?

When the dawn birds had only begun, he came to the village. The huts were there; the street stood dusty and pale in the daybreak. A few monkeys, crying like children, were perched on the forge of Ofei the blacksmith. The palm branches in the sacred grove lifted and swayed in the faint wind of morning, and beyond the village the brown river moaned as it had done eternally.

That was all. Otherwise, silence. Adamo stood at the edge of the forest, looking at his village and knowing, without thinking it, that no one was there.

Then he heard a voice high and quavering as a bird's—an old woman's voice. Soon she came out of one of the huts, walking stooped over, a mud-coloured cloth around her waist, but none around her breasts, for the parts that had once proclaimed her womanhood and had made milk for her children now hung flat and leathery, not worth covering any more. Adamo recognized her.

"Grandmother——" he said, for although she was not his grandmother, it made little difference.

The old woman stopped and peered around, as though she had been momentarily expecting a voice, but now that it had come she was confused and did not know how to reply. Then she saw him.

"It is——" she hesitated. "Man or spirit, I cannot tell."

He told her his name, and although she pretended to recognize him, he felt sure she did not. He asked her then about his family, scarcely knowing whether he could believe her or not, for her mind was light, almost departed. But she answered clearly enough.

"They are gone," she said, in the strangely gloating way the old have, as though the whole course of events could have been avoided had the young paid heed. "They are either dead or gone. There was a sickness—a long time ago, I think, although I cannot remember so well. Many people died. I do not know who died. There were too many to remember. The others left. Went away. My own family was all dead, but the others tried to persuade me to go with them. I wouldn't go. No. I wouldn't go. Go away, I told them, go away and see what happens. I will stay where I belong, in my village. So they went. I never thought they would really go. But they did."

Now Adamo began to shiver as though a chill had made each of his muscles work against the others. He questioned her patiently, precisely, saying over and over the names of his mother and his father.

"I am not sure," the old woman said. "I think—wait—that would be Afua, the daughter of Bona Ampadu?"

"That is the woman. My mother."

"I think"—the old woman struggled to remember—"I think she died. She and her husband. And—was it?—two daughters and four sons."

"Three sons," Adamo said dully. "If they died, it was three sons. I am the other."

"At least you have come back," the old woman said pettishly. "Not like those cowards who ran away. I told them, but of course they would not listen. If we die elsewhere, I said, how are the spirits of our ancestors ever to find us? Tell me that, I said. But they would not listen."

Adamo, staring at her, did not believe. He could not believe that the spirits of all the dead any longer remained in this place, as the old woman hoped. It seemed to him that the living who had gone from the village had taken with them the ancestral spirits, for their own protection. Whether his parents were alive or dead, they were gone— they had somehow been taken away. The village to him now was deserted as it could not have been had it been empty only of tangible life. The chain that linked endlessly into the past had been broken.

Adamo stood looking at the huts, at the old woman, seeing nothing. Then he turned and ran through the village until he reached his father's hut. He entered and lay down on the floor, not violently but quietly, like a man settling himself for sleep. He was determined to die because he could not think what else to do. Dead, he might find his people.

When the third morning came, his rigid limbs stirred stiffly, his head turned, his nostrils dilated because he smelled food. A betrayal, although she had meant it well. The old woman had crept up to the hut door in the night and left a bowl of goat milk and a dish of fried plantains. Adamo, sobbing despair at his body, rose shakily from the hut floor and bolted the food.

So his belly committed him to life. He went to the river and washed. Then he talked to the old woman and spent the rest of the day gathering firewood for her. When he had accumulated a large pile of dry branches, she assured him it would be enough, for she would not live long. Adamo took both her withered hands in his, looked one last time into the vague and watery eyes that were nonetheless the eyes of one of his people, and walked back into the forest.

He never knew how far he went or where. He drank from brackish pools, scooping the lime-green scum away. Fevered, he shouted and burned, and when the evil yielded he lay down and covered himself with palm boughs while the sweat lasted. A bush rat crossed his path and he killed it with his machete and ate it, sucking even the frail red bones. He came to villages where he was fed as a madman, but no one had seen his people—they had not passed this way. Adamo found a stony road and followed it until his feet were crusted with hard mud formed of the dust and his blood.

When finally he came to a town, his weariness was over-come by his astonishment, for the full streets jangled with lorries and the shops shone with a greater wealth of new knives and patterned cloth than Adamo had known existed. He strolled and gazed. A few people laughed, but he did not realize they were laughing at him, wide-eyed and filthy, his loincloth in shreds.

In an open field at the edge of the town, men were walking to and fro with guns. At dusk, when the soldiers were sitting outside the long huts, gossiping and rolling dice, Adamo ventured closer. One of the men was cleaning a white leather strap fixed to a drum. The drum was fascinat-ing to Adamo. He knew many drums used by his people, but this kind he had never seen before. He touched it curiously with his fingertips, and the soldier, laughing, handed him the sticks and showed him how to use them.

Adamo and the drum found one another. His fingers sensed some way of expressing what his mind and speech could only grope after and fail to grasp. The strange drum uttered to him the voice he now heard only in dreams, the sorrowing of someone once inexpressibly dear to him, some-one whose face he could not now visualize however hard he tried.

When the soldier reached out for the sticks, Adamo would not relinquish them and the soldier grew angry and alarmed, for he could see an officer approaching. He grabbed Adamo roughly by the shoulder.

"Here—wait a moment," Captain Fossey said. "He's not bad. Who is he?"

Adamo was startled by the alien voice, for he knew no English. He had seen white men before, but only at a distance. He wanted to run, but the soldier caught his wrist.

"He thinks you would make a drummer. He would teach you. How would you like to stay with us, bush boy?"

So it was that Adamo, who was not aware that he was an African, found himself a private in a West African regiment, having agreed to serve for five years his country, whose name he did not know.

He was given khaki shorts, a jacket with brass buttons, heavy boots, a red fez with a black tassel. He was given food, too, three times a day. But he had no idea what was expected of him, so he did everything wrong, and the men who gave commands became angry. Adamo slept badly, and his dreams filled him with emptiness, like a starving man's belly bloated with air.

One evening a short sturdy man with an enormous stomach clumped into the barracks and unslung his pack onto the cot beside Adamo's. He gave the boy a quizzical glance.

"Where from you?"

Adamo did not speak any pidgin, so he could only shake his head. The other man laughed and spoke in his own tongue, which was Adamo's as well.

"We have men of ten different tongues in this army, bush boy. And the white officers don't speak any of them. You must learn English now, if you want to get along. I myself will teach you."

Adamo's stiff smile loosened, became real. He rose, stretched, towered, held out both his hands.

"Yes—you will teach me," he said, still shyly but with certainty, for now he saw this was what was meant to happen. "You will tell me, and I will learn everything that must be done."

The others yelped with laughter. "Manu is the clever one! Hear the Big Drum who drums his own praises. Watch out, boy, he'll have you cleaning his kit and thanking him for the privilege."

Manu was the regimental bass drummer. His nickname came not only from his instrument but from his paunch and his jovial pomposity. He had just come back from leave. He told them the news of his family, and Adamo listened, too, for the hearty voice and belched laughter seemed to be for him as well. Then Manu began to scold the others.

"What have you done for this boy, scoundrels? Nothing. Lartey, when you joined the army, I saved you a thousand times—have you forgotten? Listen to the Big Drum, you small and little drummers——"

And so, with their duties assigned by Manu, they began to show Adamo what to do, and to protect him from his mistakes. When he did not understand Captain Fossey or Sergeant Sarpong, the others translated unobtrusively, and after a while he recognized the standard commands himself. He cleaned Manu's boots and even polished the brass on the great drum. The bandsmen took this as a joke, and Manu himself sometimes chortled in the depths of his throat, but Adamo did not mind. "Big Drum" seemed too familiar a name, so he called Manu "uncle".

From Captain Fossey, who in Adamo's eyes was the head of the army, the boy learned how to play the parade drum. From Sergeant Sarpong, the regimental drum major, a gaunt and haughty giant of a man, he learned how to march, how to sling his drum at the proper angle, how to watch the baton signal without appearing to do so. The daily drill was not boring to him. With each repetition, Adamo became more confident.

When he finished his basic training, and was proficient enough as a drummer, Adamo was issued with the bandsman's scarlet bolero trimmed with gold, and the square leopardskin apron the regimental drummers wore. He took fanatical care of his uniform and spent hours in cleaning and polishing.

The day came when Adamo was permitted to march with the regimental band, a drummer among the drummers. First came Sergeant Sarpong, tall as a tree, his baton aloft. Then the ranks of drummers, Adamo marching beside rangy Afutu and Botsio with his wrinkled face. Behind them came the Big Drum, Manu, wearing atop his uniform his magnificent mottled leopardskin. Then came the brass section, the horns blaring and bursting with the march tunes. And after the band, the close ranks of soldiers, the clacking boots, the bright bayonets. All the young warriors who now were not strangers to Adamo.

Captain Fossey was pleased at the speed with which Adamo learned.

"I can always tell a promising youngster," he confided to his colleagues. "Keen as mustard, he is."

Captain Fossey's tour of duty here had not been particularly encouraging. He was a ginger-haired, slightly plump Englishman of lower-middle-class origin, a man who had risen from the ranks. This in itself was bad enough, but the bandmaster also had the uncomfortable suspicion that his fellow officers regarded his branch of military activity as not quite manly.

Sometimes Captain Fossey looked at the lanky loose-limbed African bandsmen and thought that they would never in their hearts understand precision. When he heard their deep laughter he wondered uneasily what they were laughing at, and when he went back to his quarters he would strip to his pink flesh and weigh himself on his bathroom scales.

He was a bachelor. The alternate complaining and tittering of the wives at the Club filled him with alarm. How could a man commit himself to regular performance with one of those? A duty, even if only for pride's sake—that was the appalling thing. He did not intend to marry.

Adamo became Captain Fossey's prize. He gave the boy encouragement and praise, for he was under the impression that this was what Adamo needed. Adamo, who had picked up a fair amount of pidgin English, would beam in evident gratitude and produce the first phrase Manu had taught him, a phrase of exceptional efficacy.

"I t'ank you, sah," he would say in his heavy voice, so much at odds with his watchful, uncertain eyes. "I t'ank you too much."

And Captain Fossey would smile, his pale mouth parting slightly, his ginger moustache upturned.

The bandmaster often detailed Adamo to do some little job for him—an hour's work in his garden or an evening spent in helping Fossey's old steward-boy to beat the carpets. These tasks Adamo performed eagerly. He never refused Captain Fossey's shilling or two, but the Englishman had the feeling that the money was not important. Loyalty was the word that rose to Fossey's mind, a sense of personal loyalty. Captain Fossey had never had loyalty directed towards his person before.

He so far relaxed his guard as to mention Adamo to Captain Appiah. Appiah was one of the few African officers in the regiment. He did not like the British officers to make conversation with him, for he felt they were being patronizing. But if they did not speak, he resented their snobbishness.

"That young drummer of mine—Adamo," Captain Fossey said. "Lot of your people must be like that, Appiah. No education, coming straight from the bush, but by gum, all he needed was a chance in life."

Captain Appiah's tense face brooded. He had grown up in the city and had done extremely well in secondary school. He did not like to hear himself equated, as he fancied Captain Fossey was doing, with Adamo. Your people, indeed.

"I do not think he was looking for a chance in life," Captain Appiah said.

"What do you mean?"

Appiah was not sure himself what he meant. He had observed Adamo on the parade ground and had seen the boy's pleasure in the endless repetitions of the drill. He knew that Adamo followed regulations to the letter. But he could not help wondering how Adamo interpreted the rules he so scrupulously obeyed.

Once when Captain Fossey was ill, Captain Appiah took kit inspection for him. When he came to Adamo, he nodded in satisfaction. Everything was neat, in order, polished. Appiah was about to walk on, when his own curiosity or some obscure malice against Captain Fossey made him stop. He spoke in Adamo's tongue so there would be no misunderstanding.

"This"—indicating the buckle on Adamo's pack—"and the boots, and the brass buttons. You clean these things. Do you know why you must do so?"

"Sah?" Adamo's eyes widened.

Captain Appiah repeated his words. He did not, as Captain Fossey might have done, imagine that Adamo would make some remark about discipline or the smartness of the company. On the contrary, he expected Adamo to reply that he did not know or that he merely did what he was told. But the young drummer, standing tall in his flawless uniform, did not answer in this way either.

"So all things will go well," Adamo said calmly, as though there could have been no possible doubt about the matter.

Less and less did Adamo enquire in the palm-wine bars and thronged streets for word of his family. He did not often think of them now. At night in the barracks, after he took off his boots and folded his clothes carefully in the prescribed way, Adamo would lie on his cot and listen to the breathing of men all around him. Then, reassured, he would sleep.

Adamo was not talkative, but he liked it when the others talked to him. Lartey, restless as a scurrying cockroach, always searching for morsels of gossip, sometimes settled briefly beside Adamo while he worked. One afternoon Lartey began to complain about Captain Fossey.

"Again he tells me I am no good, not a soldier. I don't say I am the bravest man in the regiment. I play a drum. I am not a man for rifles. But what is he? Remember when a detachment was sent to stop the riots upcountry? Our big man heard that the band was going to be sent, too, and you should have heard him. What if a spear happened to slit a drum? Terrible! He was so worried about the drums he would place his hands over his own belly whenever he spoke of it. Then, when we were not sent, he said what a pity—we would have given heart to the men."

Lartey spluttered with laughter, and Adamo laughed too, companionably. Although he and Lartey had the same mother-tongue, Adamo was never quite clear about the other man's meaning, but he took it on faith, sensing from the voice tone what response was expected. Lartey gave him an oblique glance.

"I don't see you in trouble with Captain Fossey, Adamo. You are always trying to please him. You like him so much?"

Adamo looked up, perplexed. "Like him?"

He had never considered the question. Fossey's skin, which was the palpitating pink of a fresh-killed animal's vital organs, the sour smell his body exuded, the voice so oddly high-pitched compared to the low hoarseness of African voices, the reddish hair which seemed to Adamo a particularly offensive colour, for he associated it with forest demons who were said to be covered with red hair—all these things were unpleasant and even repulsive, but in no way significant. Adamo shrugged and resumed his work.

"He spoke, and many listened," he said, "and then I was a drummer among the drummers. His word has power—that I know."

Lartey looked at Adamo strangely and went away to talk to someone else.

Now when Adamo heard, as he still occasionally did in sleep, the muttering river, the soft slow woman voice, the voices of gods and grandsires, he would be frightened by their questioning and mourning, until they faded and a new voice, high and metallic, alien but not unknown, gained command.

Here, Adamo. You are here.

And the man Adamo, sleeping with his legs clenched up to his belly and his long hard arms wrapped tightly around his chest, would sigh, his limbs and muscles unfolding like leaves, and would mercifully cease to dream.

Captain Fossey went on leave each year, but he returned. Once, coming back with a resurgence of ambition, he decided that the regimental band could play at Club dances, and for months he sweated with his troops through campaigns of waltzes, slow foxtrots and even the African highlife tunes. Dutifully the bandsmen blew and beat a dreary path through the ballroom music, but when they played highlife their verve astounded the officers and wives. Captain Fossey was plied with compliments which he accepted as his basic due although he was aware that the troops had actually taken over while he acted merely as a kind of armchair general.

Adamo developed a skill in highlife which became the boast of the entire band. When a number was finished he would throw down his sticks and collapse over the kettle drum in laughter and exhaustion, while Manu clapped him on the shoulder and Lartey whistled and in the background Captain Fossey's voice tinkled high above the hubbub—"Jolly good, Adamo. Well done." In the years of Adamo's service, the learning of highlife was the most important innovation that occurred.

One afternoon Captain Fossey sent for Adamo. The band-master sat in his office, his puffy hands fiddling with an assortment of papers on his desk. Adamo stood smartly to attention.

"I wanted to see you," Captain Fossey began, pulling a few hairs out of his ginger moustache, "because I'll be leaving soon. Posted back to England."

He wondered if Adamo would express regret at his leaving. The boy looked puzzled but that was all. Annoyed at himself for having bothered to think of it, Captain Fossey continued more brusquely.

"A lot of officers are being posted, with independence coming up. You'll have your own chaps as officers, God help you. Thought I'd better get this settled before I go. Your five years' service time is up this month."

Adamo's face retained its composure. He stood very

straight, his big hands loose at his sides, his patient eyes waiting.

"Yes, sah."

Adamo's comprehension of English was slight at the best of times, but now, with Captain Fossey's apparent agitation, he could not understand one word. He was anxious and upset because he sensed these feelings in the bandmaster. But he was still confident that the way would be revealed and he would discover what was expected, what task would be required to restore the harmonious order of things.

Captain Fossey sighed. Having hankered for England so long, he now found he did not want to return. He remembered the damp and the cold, the cockiness and terrifying poise of the English bandsmen. Nostalgically, he recalled the ease of his life here, the devotion of men like Adamo. Would Adamo show the same loyalty to the next bandmaster?

"You can always sign up again, but I don't know that I'd advise it, Adamo. Army's liable to undergo all sorts of changes. One just doesn't know what will happen. Men promoted far too fast, from the ranks. I shouldn't say it, perhaps, but there it is. You've shown a talent for highlife. Not long ago I met the leader of a local highlife band, and— well, actually, I put in a word for you. He's short of a drummer. You can find him any evening at the Moon Club."

It seemed to Adamo that the matter could not be such a heavy one after all, for Captain Fossey had calmed now. Adamo relaxed also and was enabled to catch words here and there, like small slippery fish in the hands. Moon Club—he knew that place. It was full of soft mocking girls and gaudy men whose knife eyes Adamo did not trust. Then he understood the command. That place was to be henceforth forbidden.

Captain Fossey glanced up expectantly. "Well, what do you say?"

"Yes, sah," Adamo said agreeably. Then, after a pause and because the officer seemed to be waiting for something more, "I t'ank you, sah."

The bandmaster smiled and waved a nonchalant hand.

"Oh, that's all right. You deserve it, Adamo."

When Appiah, who was now a major, handed over the discharge papers, Adamo frowned questioningly.

"I beg you, sah—what dis t'ing?"

"Discharge papers," Appiah said irritably, for he was overworked these days. "You know, you applied for them through Captain Fossey."

He looked up, about to dismiss the man curtly, but when he saw Adamo's face he changed his mind and spoke in Adamo's own language.

"You are free to leave the army now. You signed on for five years, and the time is over. Captain Fossey said he thought you could get work with a highlife band. That's all. You can go."

Slowly, Adamo put the papers in his pocket. Then he saluted and left Major Appiah's office without a word.

He walked back to the barracks, and it was almost night. Tribes of white egrets were flying back to the baobab trees where they slept. Through the clash and clatter of the city's cars and voices, the families of frogs in the nearby lagoon could be heard beginning the throaty trilling that would go on until morning. The thin screeching of the cicada clan came from the *niim* branches now stirring with the first breeze of evening. The bandsmen had left the barracks for dinner. Adamo entered quietly and sat down on his cot.

He sat without moving, his arms limp at his sides. Finally he rose and pulled out his kitbag. He went through it, touching its contents lightly with his hands, pocketing a few things apparently at random, leaving others. Then, as though tiring of it, he shoved it away and went out of the barracks, as deliberately as he had entered. And now, outside, it was dark.

Adamo walked across the parade ground, down a road fringed with well-trimmed bougainvillaea and gardens that boasted weak-coloured zinnias. His feet seemed heavy to him, not from his boots, for he had somehow forgotten that he wore boots, but as though they were encrusted with mud formed of dust and his own blood. His head hurt and his shoulders ached. No wonder, for he had been walking such a long time. He reached out one of his hands—that hard-skinned hand was Adamo's—and the plumed *niim* leaves came away in his fingers. He scattered the leaves on the road, some on this side, some on that side, as though they had been the sacred *summe* leaves scattered in the grove. He thought he cried out, but his voice made no sound.

There were no voices to be heard, neither around him nor inside his head. There were no people in this place, no known voices. None to tell or guide, none even to mourn. Only his own voice which had strangely lost the power of sound, his silent voice splitting his lungs with its cry.

Captain Fossey's bungalow was set in a slight hollow, surrounded by flowering hibiscus with pink tongue-like petals. Adamo knocked, and when the steward-boy came, Adamo asked to see the officer.

Fossey came to the door in his bath-robe, a flowing sea-green silk. He was annoyed at being disturbed while dressing, but when he saw it was Adamo, his expression became a little milder, even anticipatory. His first thought was that Adamo had obtained the job and that he was coming now to express his gratitude.

It was his last thought as well, for within a second Adamo's knife had pierced the pink flesh of Captain Fossey's throat.

Major Appiah touched with distaste the iron bars of the cell door. *Iron, cold iron, is master of men all.* A line from something in school. This iron was slimily warm to the fingers. The whole place was stifling, the damp air foul with the stench of sweat and urine. Major Appiah tapped on the cell bars once more. The man lying in the cell lifted his head.

The officer searched Adamo's face, but Adamo was not

there. The face might have been shaped of inert clay. All at once it mattered to Major Appiah to know.

"Adamo—why? Why?"

Adamo's voice was slow and even, and he spoke in his own tongue.

"He would have made me go. Now he is gone."

Then Adamo's face, curiously striped by the iron bars, lost its empty look and his voice was a quick high cry of pain.

"What did I not do? All he spoke was done, that no evil would come. Was it not enough?"

Appiah could not reply, for Adamo's desolation was unreachable. Adamo stood silently for a moment. Then he cried out again, almost incredulously, as though he refused what he spoke.

"My father's knife—to spill his power? My hand, mine?" The voice faltered. "Oh, what may follow? You will tell me what I must do. I would not bring harm upon them all—tell Manu I would not do that. I will do whatever you say, whatever must be done. Only——"

In the anguished eyes a question burned and trembled. Finally he was able to express it.

"I will stay?"

Major Appiah had come to tell Adamo when the trial would be held, perhaps even to prepare the man for the inevitability of the verdict. But he said none of these things, for he saw now that they could make no difference at all. Adamo would discover soon enough what ritual would be required for restitution. Perhaps even that made little difference. It was not death that Adamo feared.

"Yes," Major Appiah said, and as he spoke he became aware of a crippling sense of weariness, as though an accumulation of centuries had been foisted upon himself, to deal with somehow. "You can stay, Adamo. You can stay as long as you live."

He turned away abruptly, and his boots drummed on the concrete corridor. He could bear anything, he felt, except the look of relief in Adamo's eyes.

Gertrude
the Governess:
or Simple Seventeen

Synopsis of Previous Chapters:
There are no Previous Chapters.

 It was a wild and stormy night on the West Coast of Scotland. This, however, is immaterial to the present story, as the scene is not laid in the West of Scotland. For the matter of that the weather was just as bad on the East Coast of Ireland.

But the scene of this narrative is laid in the South of England and takes place in and around Knotacentinum Towers (pronounced as if written Nosham Taws), the seat of Lord Knotacent (pronounced as if written Nosh).

But it is not necessary to pronounce either of these names in reading them.

Nosham Taws was a typical English home. The main part of the house was an Elizabethan structure of warm red brick, while the elder portion, of which the Earl was inordinately proud, still

STEPHEN
LEACOCK

showed the outlines of a Norman Keep, to which had been added a Lancastrian Jail and a Plantagenet Orphan Asylum. From the house in all directions stretched magnificent woodland and park with oaks and elms of immemorial antiquity, while nearer the house stood raspberry bushes and geranium plants which had been set out by the Crusaders.

About the grand old mansion the air was loud with the chirping of thrushes, the cawing of partridges and the clear sweet note of the rook, while deer, antelope, and other quadrupeds strutted about the lawn so tame as to eat off the sun-dial. In fact, the place was a regular menagerie.

From the house downwards through the park stretched a beautiful broad avenue laid out by Henry VII.

Lord Nosh stood upon the hearthrug of the library. Trained diplomat and statesman as he was, his stern aristocratic face was upside down with fury.

"Boy," he said, "you shall marry this girl or I disinherit you. You are no son of mine."

Young Lord Ronald, erect before him, flung back a glance as defiant as his own.

"I defy you," he said. "Hence forth you are no father of mine. I will get another. I will marry none but a woman I can love. This girl that we have never seen—"

"Fool," said the Earl, "would you throw aside our estate and name of a thousand years? The girl, I am told, is beautiful; her aunt is willing; they are French; pah! they understand such things in France."

"But your reason—"

"I give no reason," said the Earl. "Listen, Ronald, I give you one month. For that time you remain here. If at the end of it you refuse me, I cut you off with a shilling."

Lord Ronald said nothing; he flung himself from the room, flung himself upon his horse and rode madly off in all directions.

As the door of the library closed upon Ronald the Earl sank into a chair. His face changed. It was no longer that of the haughty nobleman, but of the hunted criminal. "He must marry the girl," he muttered. "Soon she will know all. Tutchemoff has escaped from Siberia. He knows and will tell. The whole of the mines pass to her, this property with it, and I—but enough." He rose, walked to the sideboard, drained a dipper full of gin and bitters, and became again a high-bred English gentleman.

It was at this moment that a high dogcart, driven by a groom in the livery of Earl Nosh, might have been seen entering the avenue of Nosham Taws. Beside him sat a young girl, scarce more than a child, in fact not nearly so big as the groom.

The apple-pie hat which she wore, surmounted with black willow plumes, concealed from view a face so face-like in its appearance as to be positively facial.

It was—need we say it—Gertrude the Governess, who was this day to enter upon her duties at Nosham Taws.

At the same time that the dogcart entered the avenue at one end there might have been seen riding down it from the other a tall young man, whose long, aristocratic face proclaimed his birth and who was mounted upon a horse with a face even longer than his own.

And who is this tall young man who draws nearer to Gertrude with every revolution of the horse? Ah, who, indeed? Ah, who, who? I wonder if any of my readers could guess that this was none other than Lord Ronald.

The two were destined to meet. Nearer and nearer they came. And then still nearer. Then for one brief moment they met. As they passed, Gertrude raised her head and directed towards the young nobleman two eyes so eye-like in their expression as to be absolutely circular, while Lord Ronald directed towards the occupant of the dogcart a gaze so gaze-like that nothing but a gazelle, or a gas-pipe, could have emulated its intensity.

Was this the dawn of love? Wait and see. Do not spoil the story.

Let us speak of Gertrude. Gertrude DeMongmorenci McFiggin had known neither father nor mother. They had both died years before she was born. Of her mother she knew nothing, save that she was French, was extremely beautiful, and that all her ancestors and even her business acquaintances had perished in the Revolution.

Yet Gertrude cherished the memory of her parents. On her breast the girl wore a locket in which was enshrined a miniature of her mother, while down her neck inside at the back hung a daguerreotype of her father. She carried a portrait of her grandmother up her sleeve and had pictures of her cousins tucked inside her boot, while beneath her— but enough, quite enough.

Of her father Gertrude knew even less. That he was a high-born English gentleman who had lived as a wanderer in many lands, this was all she knew. His only legacy to Gertrude had been a Russian grammar, a Roumanian phrase-book, a theodolite, and a work on mining engineering.

From her earliest infancy Gertrude had been brought up by her aunt. Her aunt had carefully instructed her in Christian principles. She had also taught her Mohammedanism to make sure.

When Gertrude was seventeen her aunt had died of hydrophobia.

The circumstances were mysterious. There had called upon her that day a strange bearded man in the costume of the Russians. After he had left, Gertrude had found her aunt in a syncope from which she passed into an apostrophe and never recovered.

To avoid scandal it was called hydrophobia. Gertrude was thus thrown upon the world. What to do? That was the problem that confronted her.

It was while musing one day upon her fate that Gertrude's eye was struck with an advertisement.

"Wanted a governess: must possess a knowledge of French, Italian, Russian, and Roumanian, Music, and Mining Engineering. Salary £1, 4 shillings and 4 pence halfpenny per annum. Apply between half-past eleven and twenty-five minutes to twelve at No. 41 A Decimal Six, Belgravia Terrace. The Countess of Nosh."

Gertrude was a girl of great natural quickness of apprehension, and she had not pondered over this announcement more than half an hour before she was struck with the extraordinary coincidence between the list of items desired and the things that she herself knew.

She duly presented herself at Belgravia Terrace before the Countess, who advanced to meet her with a charm which at once placed the girl at her ease.

"You are proficient in French?" she asked.

"*Oh, oui,*" said Gertrude modestly.

"And Italian?" continued the Countess.

"*Oh, si,*" said Gertrude.

"And German?" said the Countess in delight.

"*Ah, ja,*" said Gertrude.

"And Russian?"

"*Yaw.*"

"And Roumanian?"

"*Jep.*"

Amazed at the girl's extraordinary proficiency in modern languages, the Countess looked at her narrowly. Where had she seen those lineaments before? She passed her hand over her brow in thought, and spit upon the floor, but no, the face baffled her.

"Enough," she said. "I engage you on the spot; tomorrow you go down to Nosham Taws and begin teaching the children. I must add that in addition you will be expected to aid the Earl with his Russian correspondence. He has large mining interests at Tschminsk."

Tschminsk! why did the simple word reverberate upon Gertrude's ears? Why? Because it was the name written in her father's hand on the title page of his book on mining. What mystery was here?

It was on the following day that Gertrude had driven up the avenue.

She descended from the dogcart, passed through a phalanx of liveried servants drawn up seven-deep, to each of whom she gave a sovereign as she passed and entered Nosham Taws.

"Welcome," said the Countess, as she aided Gertrude to carry her trunk upstairs.

The girl presently descended and was ushered into the library, where she was presented to the Earl. As soon as the Earl's eye fell upon the face of the new governess he started visibly. Where had he seen those lineaments? Where was it? At the races? or the theatre? on a bus? No. Some subtler thread of memory was stirring in his mind. He strode hastily to the sideboard, drained a dipper and a half of brandy, and became again the perfect English gentleman.

While Gertrude has gone to the nursery to make the acquaintance of the two tiny golden-haired children who are to be her charges, let us say something here of the Earl and his son.

Lord Nosh was the perfect type of the English nobleman and statesman. The years that he had spent in the diplomatic service at Constantinople, St Petersburg, and Salt Lake City had given to him a peculiar finesse and noblesse, while his long residence at St Helena, Pitcairn Island, and Hamilton, Ontario, had rendered him impervious to external impressions. As deputy paymaster of the militia of the country he had seen something of the sterner side of military life, while his hereditary office of Groom of the Sunday Breeches had brought him into direct contact with Royalty itself. His passion for outdoor sports endeared him to his tenants. A keen sportsman, he excelled in foxhunting, doghunting, pig-killing, bat-catching and the pastimes of his class.

In this latter respect Lord Ronald took after his father. From the start the lad had shown the greatest promise. At Eton he had made a splendid showing at battledore and shuttlecock, and at Cambridge had been first in his class at needlework. Already his name was whispered in connection with the All England ping-pong championship, a triumph which would undoubtedly carry with it a seat in Parliament.

Thus was Gertrude the Governess installed at Nosham Taws.

The days and the weeks sped past.

The simple charm of the beautiful orphan girl attracted all hearts. Her two little pupils became her slaves. "Me loves oo," the little Rasehellfrida would say, leaning her golden head in Gertrude's lap. Even the servants loved her. The head gardener would bring a bouquet of beautiful roses to her room before she was up, the second gardener a bunch of early cauliflowers, the third a spray of late asparagus, and even the tenth and eleventh a sprig of mangel-wurzel or an armful of hay. Her room was full of gardeners all the time, while at evening the aged butler, touched at the friendless girl's loneliness, would tap softly at her door to bring her a rye whisky and seltzer or a box of Pittsburg Stogies. Even the dumb creatures seemed to admire her in their own dumb way. The dumb rooks settled on her shoulder and every dumb dog around the place followed her.

And Ronald! ah, Ronald! Yes, indeed! They had met. They had spoken.

"What a dull morning," Gertrude had said. *"Quel triste matin! Was für ein allerverdamnter Tag!"*

"Beastly," Ronald had answered.

"Beastly!!" The word rang in Gertrude's ears all day.

After that they were constantly together. They played tennis and ping-pong in the day, and in the evening, in accordance with the stiff routine of the place, they sat down with the Earl and Countess to twenty-five-cent poker, and later still they sat together on the verandah and watched the moon sweeping in great circles around the horizon.

It was not long before Gertrude realized that Lord Ronald felt towards her a warmer feeling than that of mere ping-pong. At times in her presence he would fall, especially after dinner, into a fit of profound subtraction.

Once at night, when Gertrude withdrew to her chamber and before seeking her pillow, prepared to retire as a preliminary to disrobing—in other words, before going to bed, she flung wide the casement (opened the window) and perceived (saw) the face of Lord Ronald. He was sitting on a thorn bush beneath her, and his upturned face wore an expression of agonized pallor.

Meantime the days passed. Life at the Taws moved in the ordinary routine of a great English household. At 7 a gong sounded for rising, at 8 a horn blew for breakfast, at 8:30 a whistle sounded for prayers, at 1 a flag was run up at halfmast for lunch, at 4 a gun was fired for afternoon tea, at 9 a first bell sounded for dressing, at 9:15 a second bell for going on dressing, while at 9:30 a rocket was sent up to indicate that dinner was ready. At midnight dinner was over, and at 1 a.m. the tolling of a bell summoned the domestics to evening prayers.

Meanwhile the month allotted by the Earl to Lord Ronald was passing away. It was already July 15, then within a day or two it was July 17, and, almost immediately afterwards, July 18.

At times the Earl, in passing Ronald in the hall, would say sternly, "Remember, boy, your consent, or I disinherit you."

And what were the Earl's thoughts of Gertrude? Here was the one drop of bitterness in the girl's cup of happiness. For some reason that she could not divine the Earl showed signs of marked antipathy.

Once as she passed the door of the library he threw a bootjack at her. On another occasion at lunch alone with her he struck her savagely across the face with a sausage.

It was her duty to translate to the Earl his Russian correspondence. She sought in it in vain for the mystery. One day a Russian telegram was handed to the Earl. Gertrude translated it to him aloud.

"Tutchemoff went to the woman. She is dead."

On hearing this the Earl became livid with fury, in fact this was the day that he struck her with the sausage.

Then one day while the Earl was absent on a bat hunt, Gertrude, who was turning over his correspondence, with that sweet feminine instinct of interest that rose superior to ill-treatment, suddenly found the key to the mystery.

Lord Nosh was not the rightful owner of the Taws. His distant cousin of the older line, the true heir, had died in a Russian prison to which the machinations of the Earl, while

Ambassador at Tschminsk, had consigned him. The daughter of this cousin was the true owner of Nosham Taws.

The family story, save only that the documents before her withheld the name of the rightful heir, lay bare to Gertrude's eye.

Strange is the heart of woman. Did Gertrude turn from the Earl with spurning? No. Her own sad fate had taught her sympathy.

Yet still the mystery remained! Why did the Earl start perceptibly each time that he looked into her face? Sometimes he started as much as four centimetres, so that one could distinctly see him do it. On such occasions he would hastily drain a dipper of rum and vichy water and become again the correct English gentleman.

The denouement came swiftly. Gertrude never forgot it.

It was the night of the great ball at Nosham Taws. The whole neighbourhood was invited. How Gertrude's heart had beat with anticipation, and with what trepidation she had overhauled her scant wardrobe in order to appear not unworthy in Lord Ronald's eyes. Her resources were poor indeed, yet the inborn genius for dress that she inherited from her French mother stood her in good stead. She twined a single rose in her hair and contrived herself a dress out of a few old newspapers and the inside of an umbrella that would have graced a court. Round her waist she bound a single braid of bagstring, while a piece of old lace that had been her mother's was suspended to her ear by a thread.

Gertrude was the cynosure of all eyes. Floating to the strains of the music she presented a picture of bright girlish innocence that no one could see undisenraptured.

The ball was at its height. It was away up!

Ronald stood with Gertrude in the shrubbery. They looked into one another's eyes.

"Gertrude," he said, "I love you."

Simple words, and yet they thrilled every fibre in the girl's costume.

"Ronald!" she said, and cast herself about his neck.

At this moment the Earl appeared standing beside them

in the moonlight. His stern face was distorted with indignation.

"So!" he said, turning to Ronald, "it appears that you have chosen!"

"I have," said Ronald with hauteur.

"You prefer to marry this penniless girl rather than the heiress I have selected for you."

Gertrude looked from father to son in amazement.

"Yes," said Ronald.

"Be it so," said the Earl, draining a dipper of gin which he carried, and resuming his calm. "Then I disinherit you. Leave this place, and never return to it."

"Come, Gertrude," said Ronald tenderly, "let us flee together."

Gertrude stood before them. The rose had fallen from her head. The lace had fallen from her ear and the bagstring had come undone from her waist. Her newspapers were crumpled beyond recognition. But dishevelled and illegible as she was, she was still mistress of herself.

"Never," she said firmly. "Ronald, you shall never make this sacrifice for me." Then to the Earl, in tones of ice, "There is a pride, sir, as great even as yours. The daughter of Metschnikoff McFiggin need crave a boon from no one."

With that she hauled from her bosom the daguerreotype of her father and pressed it to her lips.

The Earl started as if shot. "That name!" he cried, "that face! that photograph! stop!"

There! There is no need to finish; my readers have long since divined it. Gertrude was the heiress.

The lovers fell into one another's arms. The Earl's proud face relaxed. "God bless you," he said. The Countess and the guests came pouring out upon the lawn. The breaking day illuminated a scene of gay congratulations.

Gertrude and Ronald were wed. Their happiness was complete. Need we say more? Yes, only this. The Earl was killed in the hunting-field a few days after. The Countess was struck by lightning. The two children fell down a well. Thus the happiness of Gertrude and Ronald was complete.

Walker Brothers Cowboy

After supper my father says, "Want to go down and see if the Lake's still there?" We leave my mother sewing under the dining-room light, making clothes for me against the opening of school. She has ripped up for this purpose an old suit and an old plaid wool dress of hers, and she has to cut and match very cleverly and also make me stand and turn for endless fittings, sweaty, itching from the hot wool, ungrateful. We leave my brother in bed in the little screened porch at the end of the front verandah, and sometimes he kneels on his bed and presses his face against the screen and calls mournfully, "Bring me an ice cream cone!" but I call back, "You will be asleep," and do not even turn my head.

Then my father and I walk gradually down a long, shabby sort of street, with Silverwoods Ice Cream signs standing on the sidewalk, outside tiny, lighted stores. This is in Tuppertown, an old town on Lake Huron, an old grain port.

ALICE
MUNRO

The street is shaded, in some places, by maple trees whose roots have cracked and heaved the sidewalk and spread out like crocodiles into the bare yards. People are sitting out, men in shirt-sleeves and undershirts and women in aprons —not people we know but if anybody looks ready to nod and say, "Warm night," my father will nod too and say something the same. Children are still playing. I don't know them either because my mother keeps my brother and me in our own yard, saying he is too young to leave it and I have to mind him. I am not so sad to watch their evening games because the games themselves are ragged, dissolving. Children, of their own will, draw apart, separate into islands of two or one under the heavy trees, occupying themselves in such solitary ways as I do all day, planting pebbles in the dirt or writing in it with a stick.

Presently we leave these yards and houses behind, we pass a factory with boarded-up windows, a lumberyard whose high wooden gates are locked for the night. Then the town falls away in a defeated jumble of sheds and small junkyards, the sidewalk gives up and we are walking on a sandy path with burdocks, plantains, humble nameless weeds all around. We enter a vacant lot, a kind of park really, for it is kept clear of junk and there is one bench with a slat missing on the back, a place to sit and look at the water. Which is generally grey in the evening, under a lightly overcast sky, no sunsets, the horizon dim. A very quiet, washing noise on the stones of the beach. Further along, towards the main part of town, there is a stretch of sand, a water slide, floats bobbing around the safe swimming area, a life guard's rickety throne. Also a long dark green building, like a roofed verandah, called the Pavilion, full of farmers and their wives, in stiff good clothes, on Sundays. That is the part of the town we used to know when we lived at Dungannon and came here three or four times a summer, to the Lake. That, and the docks where we would go and look at the grain boats, ancient, rusty, wallowing, making us wonder how they got past the breakwater let alone to Fort William.

Tramps hang around the docks and occasionally on these evenings wander up the dwindling beach and climb the shifting, precarious path boys have made, hanging onto dry bushes, and say something to my father which, being frightened of tramps, I am too alarmed to catch. My father says he is a bit hard up himself. "I'll roll you a cigarette if it's any use to you," he says, and he shakes tobacco out carefully on one of the thin butterfly papers, flicks it with his tongue, seals it and hands it to the tramp who takes it and walks away. My father also rolls and lights and smokes one cigarette of his own.

He tells me how the Great Lakes came to be. All where Lake Huron is now, he says, used to be flat land, a wide flat plain. Then came the ice, creeping down from the north, pushing deep into the low places. Like *that*—and he shows me his hand with his spread fingers pressing the rock-hard ground where we are sitting. His fingers make hardly any impression at all and he says, "Well, the old ice cap had a lot more power behind it than this hand has." And then the ice went back, shrank back towards the North Pole where it came from, and left its fingers of ice in the deep places it had gouged, and ice turned to lakes and there they were today. They were *new*, as time went. I try to see that plain before me, dinosaurs walking on it, but I am not able even to imagine the shore of the Lake when the Indians were there, before Tuppertown. The tiny share we have of time appalls me, though my father seems to regard it with tranquillity. Even my father, who sometimes seems to me to have been at home in the world as long as it has lasted, has really lived on this earth only a little longer than I have, in terms of all the time there has been to live in. He has not known a time, any more than I, when automobiles and electric lights did not at least exist. He was not alive when this century started. I will be barely alive—old, old—when it ends. I do not like to think of it. I wish the Lake to be always just a lake, with the safe-swimming floats marking it, and the breakwater and the lights of Tuppertown.

My father has a job, selling for Walker Brothers. This is a firm that sells almost entirely in the country, the back country. Sunshine, Boylesbridge, Turnaround—that is all his territory. Not Dungannon where we used to live, Dungannon is too near town and my mother is grateful for that. He sells cough medicine, iron tonic, corn plasters, laxatives, pills for female disorders, mouth wash, shampoo, liniment, salves, lemon and orange and raspberry concentrate for making refreshing drinks, vanilla, food colouring, black and green tea, ginger, cloves and other spices, rat poison. He has a song about it, with these two lines:

> And have all liniments and oils,
> For everything from corns to
> boils. . . .

Not a very funny song, in my mother's opinion. A pedlar's song, and that is what he is, a pedlar knocking at backwoods kitchens. Up until last winter we had our own business, a fox farm. My father raised silver foxes and sold their pelts to the people who make them into capes and coats and muffs. Prices fell, my father hung on hoping they would get better next year, and they fell again, and he hung on one more year and one more and finally it was not possible to hang on any more, we owed everything to the feed company. I have heard my mother explain this, several times, to Mrs. Oliphant who is the only neighbour she talks to. (Mrs. Oliphant also has come down in the world, being a schoolteacher who married the janitor.) We poured all we had into it, my mother says, and we came out with nothing. Many people could say the same thing, these days, but my mother has no time for the national calamity, only ours. Fate has flung us onto a street of poor people (it does not matter that we were poor before, that was a different sort of poverty), and the only way to take this, as she sees it, is with dignity, with bitterness, with no reconciliation. No bathroom with a claw-footed tub and a flush toilet is going to comfort her, nor water on tap and sidewalks past the house and milk in bottles, not even the two movie theatres and the Venus Restaurant and Woolworths so marvellous it has live birds singing in its fan-cooled corners and fish as tiny as fingernails, as bright as moons, swimming in its green tanks. My mother does not care.

In the afternoons she often walks to Simon's Grocery and takes me with her to help carry things. She wears a good dress, navy blue with little flowers, sheer, worn over a navy-blue slip. Also a summer hat of white straw, pushed down on the side of the head, and white shoes I have just whitened on a newspaper on the back steps. I have my hair freshly done in long damp curls which the dry air will fortunately soon loosen, a stiff large hair-ribbon on top of my head. This is entirely different from going out after supper with my father. We have not walked past two houses before I feel we have become objects of universal ridicule. Even the dirty words chalked on the sidewalk are laughing at us. My mother does not seem to notice. She walks serenely like a lady shopping, like a *lady* shopping, past the housewives in loose beltless dresses torn under the arms. With me her creation, wretched curls and flaunting hair bow, scrubbed knees and white socks—all I do not want to be. I loathe even my name when she says it in public, in a voice so high, proud and ringing, deliberately different from the voice of any other mother on the street.

My mother will sometimes carry home, for a treat, a brick of ice cream—pale Neapolitan; and because we have no refrigerator in our house we wake my brother and eat it at once in the dining room, always darkened by the wall of the house next door. I spoon it up tenderly, leaving the chocolate till last, hoping to have some still to eat when my brother's dish is empty. My mother tries then to imitate the conversations we used to have at Dungannon, going back to our earliest, most leisurely days before my brother was born, when she would give me a little tea and a lot of milk in a cup like hers and we would sit out on the step facing the pump, the lilac tree, the fox pens beyond. She is not able to keep from mentioning those days. "Do you remember when we put you in your sled and Major pulled you?" (Major our dog, that we had to leave with neighbours when we moved.) "Do you remember your sandbox outside the kitchen window?" I pretend to remember far less than I do, wary of being trapped into sympathy or any unwanted emotion.

My mother has headaches. She often has to lie down. She lies on my brother's narrow bed in the little screened porch, shaded by heavy branches. "I look up at that tree and I think I am at home," she says.

"What you need," my father tells her, "is some fresh air and a drive in the country." He means for her to go with him, on his Walker Brothers route.

That is not my mother's idea of a drive in the country.

"Can I come?"

"Your mother might want you for trying on clothes."

"I'm beyond sewing this afternoon," my mother says.

"I'll take her then. Take both of them, give you a rest."

What is there about us that people need to be given a rest from? Never mind. I am glad enough to find my brother and make him go to the toilet and get us both into the car, our knees unscrubbed, my hair unringleted. My father brings from the house his two heavy brown suitcases, full of bottles, and sets them on the back seat. He wears a white shirt, brilliant in the sunlight, a tie, light trousers belonging to his summer suit (his other suit is black, for funerals, and belonged to my uncle before he died) and a creamy straw hat. His salesman's outfit, with pencils clipped in the shirt pocket. He goes back once again, probably to say goodbye to my mother, to ask her if she is sure she doesn't want to come, and hear her say, "No. No thanks, I'm better just to lie here with my eyes closed." Then we are backing out of the driveway with the rising hope of adventure, just the little hope that takes you over the bump into the street, the hot air starting to move, turning into a breeze, the houses growing less and less familiar as we follow the short cut my father knows, the quick way out of town. Yet what is there

waiting for us all afternoon but hot hours in stricken farmyards, perhaps a stop at a country store and three ice cream
cones or bottles of pop, and my father singing? The one he
made up about himself has a title—"The Walker Brothers
Cowboy"—and it starts out like this:

> Old Ned Fields, he now is dead,
> So I am ridin' the route instead. . . .

Who is Ned Fields? The man he has replaced, surely, and
if so he really is dead; yet my father's voice is mournful-jolly,
making his death some kind of nonsense, a comic calamity.
"Wisht I was back on the Rio Grande, plungin' through the
dusky sand." My father sings most of the time while driving
the car. Even now, heading out of town, crossing the bridge
and taking the sharp turn onto the highway, he is humming
something, mumbling a bit of a song to himself, just tuning
up, really, getting ready to improvise, for out along the
highway we pass the Baptist Camp, the Vacation Bible
Camp, and he lets loose:

> Where are the Baptists, where are the Baptists,
>   where are all the Baptists today?
> They're down in the water, in Lake Huron water,
>   with their sins all a-gittin' washed away.

My brother takes this for straight truth and gets up on his
knees trying to see down to the Lake. "I don't see any
Baptists," he says accusingly. "Neither do I, son," says my
father. "I told you, they're down in the Lake."

No roads paved when we left the highway. We have to
roll up the windows because of dust. The land is flat,
scorched, empty. Bush lots at the back of the farms hold
shade, black pine-shade like pools nobody can ever get to.
We bump up a long lane and at the end of it what could look
more unwelcoming, more deserted than the tall unpainted
farmhouse with grass growing uncut right up to the front

door, green blinds down and a door upstairs opening on nothing but air? Many houses have this door, and I have never yet been able to find out why. I ask my father and he says they are for walking in your sleep. *What?* Well if you happen to be walking in your sleep and you want to step outside. I am offended, seeing too late that he is joking, as usual, but my brother says sturdily, "If they did that they would break their necks."

The nineteen-thirties. How much this kind of farmhouse, this kind of afternoon, seem to me to belong to that one decade in time, just as my father's hat does, his bright flared tie, our car with its wide running board (an Essex, and long past its prime). Cars somewhat like it, many older, none dustier, sit in the farmyards. Some are past running and have their doors pulled off, their seats removed for use on porches. No living things to be seen, chickens or cattle. Except dogs. There are dogs, lying in any kind of shade they can find, dreaming, their lean sides rising and sinking rapidly. They get up when my father opens the car door, he has to speak to them. "Nice boy, there's a boy, nice old boy." They quiet down, go back to their shade. He should know how to quiet animals, he has held desperate foxes with tongs around their necks. One gentling voice for the dogs and another, rousing, cheerful, for calling at doors. "Hello there, Missus, it's the Walker Brothers man and what are you out of today?" A door opens, he disappears. Forbidden to follow, forbidden even to leave the car, we can just wait and wonder what he says. Sometimes trying to make my mother laugh he pretends to be himself in a farm kitchen, spreading out his sample case. "Now then, Missus, are you troubled with parasitic life? Your children's scalps, I mean. All those crawly little things we're too polite to mention that show up on the heads of the best of families? Soap alone is useless, kerosene is not too nice a perfume, but I have here—" Or else, "Believe me, sitting and driving all day the way I do I *know* the value of these fine pills. Natural relief. A problem common to old folks, too, once their days of activity are over

—How about you, Grandma?" He would wave the imaginary box of pills under my mother's nose and she would laugh finally, unwillingly. "He doesn't say that really, does he?" I said, and she said no of course not, he was too much of a gentleman.

One yard after another, then, the old cars, the pumps, dogs, views of grey barns and falling-down sheds and un-turning windmills. The men, if they are working in the fields, are not in any fields that we can see. The children are far away, following dry creek beds or looking for blackberries, or else they are hidden in the house, spying at us through cracks in the blinds. The car seat has grown slick with our sweat. I dare my brother to sound the horn, wanting to do it myself but not wanting to get the blame. He knows better. We play *I Spy*, but it is hard to find many colours. Grey for the barns and sheds and toilets and houses, brown for the yard and fields, black or brown for the dogs. The rusting cars show rainbow patches, in which I strain to pick out purple or green; likewise I peer at doors for shreds of old peeling paint, maroon or yellow. We can't play with letters, which would be better, because my brother is too young to spell. The game disintegrates anyway. He claims my colours are not fair, and wants extra turns.

In one house no door opens, though the car is in the yard. My father knocks and whistles, calls, "Hullo there! Walker Brothers man!" but there is not a stir of reply anywhere. This house has no porch, just a bare, slanting slab of cement on which my father stands. He turns around, searching the barnyard, the barn whose mow must be empty because you can see the sky through it, and finally he bends to pick up his suitcases. Just then a window is opened upstairs, a white pot appears on the sill, is tilted over and its contents splash down the outside wall. The window is not directly above my father's head, so only a stray splash would catch him. He picks up his suitcases with no particular hurry and walks, no longer whistling, to the car. "Do you know what that was?" I say to my brother. "*Pee*." He laughs and laughs.

My father rolls and lights a cigarette before he starts the car. The window has been slammed down, the blind drawn, we never did see a hand or face. "Pee, pee," sings my brother ecstatically. "Somebody dumped down pee!" "Just don't tell your mother that," my father says. "She isn't liable to see the joke." "Is it in your song?" my brother wants to know. My father says no but he will see what he can do to work it in.

I notice in a little while that we are not turning in any more lanes, though it does not seem to me that we are headed home. "Is this the way to Sunshine?" I ask my father, and he answers, "No ma'am it's not." "Are we still in your territory?" He shakes his head. "We're going *fast*," my brother says approvingly, and in fact we are bouncing along through dry puddle-holes so that all the bottles in the suitcases clink together and gurgle promisingly.

Another lane, a house, also unpainted, dried to silver in the sun.

"I thought we were out of your territory."

"We are."

"Then what are we going in here for?"

"You'll see."

In front of the house a short, sturdy woman is picking up washing, which had been spread on the grass to bleach and dry. When the car stops she stares at it hard for a moment, bends to pick up a couple more towels to add to the bundle under her arm, comes across to us and says in a flat voice, neither welcoming nor unfriendly, "Have you lost your way?"

My father takes his time getting out of the car. "I don't think so," he says. "I'm the Walker Brothers man."

"George Golley is our Walker Brothers man," the woman says, "and he was out here no more than a week ago. Oh, my Lord God," she says harshly, "it's you."

"It was, the last time I looked in the mirror," my father says. The woman gathers all the towels in front of her and holds on to them tightly, pushing them against her stomach as if it hurt. "Of all the people I never thought to see. And telling me you were the Walker Brothers man."

"I'm sorry if you were looking forward to George Golley," my father says humbly.

"And look at me, I was prepared to clean the hen-house. You'll think that's just an excuse but it's true. I don't go round looking like this every day." She is wearing a farmer's straw hat, through which pricks of sunlight penetrate and float on her face, a loose, dirty print smock and running shoes. "Who are those in the car, Ben? They're not yours?"

"Well I hope and believe they are," my father says, and tells our names and ages. "Come on, you can get out. This is Nora, Miss Cronin. Nora, you better tell me, is it still Miss, or have you got a husband hiding in the woodshed?"

"If I had a husband that's not where I'd keep him, Ben," she says, and they both laugh, her laugh abrupt and somewhat angry. "You'll think I got no manners, as well as being dressed like a tramp," she says. "Come on in out of the sun. It's cool in the house."

We go across the yard ("Excuse me taking you in this way but I don't think the front door has been opened since Papa's funeral, I'm afraid the hinges might drop off"), up the porch steps, into the kitchen, which really is cool, high-ceilinged, the blinds of course down, a simple, clean, threadbare room with waxed worn linoleum, potted geraniums, drinking-pail and dipper, a round table with scrubbed oilcloth. In spite of the cleanness, the wiped and swept surfaces, there is a faint sour smell—maybe of the dishrag or in the tin dipper or the oilcloth, or the old lady, because there is one, sitting in an easy chair under the clock shelf. She turns her head slightly in our direction and says, "Nora? Is that company?"

"Blind," says Nora in a quick explaining voice to my father. Then, "You won't guess who it is, Momma. Hear his voice."

My father goes to the front of her chair and bends and says hopefully, "Afternoon, Mrs. Cronin."

"Ben Jordan," says the old lady with no surprise. "You

haven't been to see us in the longest time. Have you been out of the country?"

My father and Nora look at each other.

"He's married, Momma," says Nora cheerfully and aggressively. "Married and got two children and here they are." She pulls us forward, makes each of us touch the old lady's dry, cool hand while she says our names in turn. Blind! This is the first blind person I have ever seen close up. Her eyes are closed, the eyelids sunk away down, showing no shape of the eyeball, just hollows. From one hollow comes a drop of silver liquid, a medicine, or a miraculous tear.

"Let me get into a decent dress," Nora says. "Talk to Momma. It's a treat for her. We hardly ever see company, do we Momma?"

"Not many makes it out this road," says the old lady placidly. "And the ones that used to be around here, our old neighbours, some of them have pulled out."

"True everywhere," my father says.

"Where's your wife then?"

"Home. She's not too fond of the hot weather, makes her feel poorly."

"Well." This is a habit of country people, old people, to say "well", meaning, "is that so?" with a little extra politeness and concern.

Nora's dress, when she appears again—stepping heavily on Cuban Heels down the stairs in the hall—is flowered more lavishly than anything my mother owns, green and yellow on brown, some sort of floating sheer crepe, leaving her arms bare. Her arms are heavy, and every bit of her skin you can see is covered with little dark freckles like measles. Her hair is short, black, coarse and curly, her teeth very white and strong. "It's the first time I knew there was such a thing as green poppies," my father says, looking at her dress.

"You would be surprised all the things you never knew," says Nora, sending a smell of cologne far and wide when she moves and displaying a change of voice to go with the dress, something more sociable and youthful. "They're not poppies anyway, they're just flowers. You go and pump me some good cold water and I'll make these children a drink." She gets down from the cupboard a bottle of Walker Brothers Orange syrup.

"You telling me you were the Walker Brothers man!"

"It's the truth, Nora. You go and look at my sample cases in the car if you don't believe me. I got the territory directly south of here."

"Walker Brothers? Is that a fact? You selling for Walker Brothers?"

"Yes ma'am."

"We always heard you were raising foxes over Dungannon way."

"That's what I was doing, but I kind of run out of luck in that business."

"So where're you living? How long've you been out selling?"

"We moved into Tuppertown. I been at it, oh, two, three months. It keeps the wolf from the door. Keeps him as far away as the back fence."

Nora laughs. "Well I guess you count yourself lucky to have the work. Isabel's husband in Brantford, he was out of work the longest time. I thought if he didn't find something soon I was going to have them all land in here to feed, and I tell you I was hardly looking forward to it. It's all I can manage with me and Momma."

"Isabel married," my father says. "Muriel married too?"

"No, she's teaching school out west. She hasn't been home for five years. I guess she finds something better to do with her holidays. I would if I was her." She gets some snapshots out of the table drawer and starts showing him. "That's Isabel's oldest boy, starting school. That's the baby sitting in her carriage. Isabel and her husband. Muriel. That's her roommate with her. That's a fellow she used to go around with, and his car. He was working in a bank out there. That's her school, it has eight rooms. She teaches Grade Five." My father shakes his head. "I can't think of her any way but when she was going to school, so shy I used to pick her up on the road—I'd be on my way to see you—and she would not say one word, not even to agree it was a nice day."

"She's got over that."

"Who are you talking about?" says the old lady.

"Muriel. I said she's got over being shy."

"She was here last summer."

"No Momma that was Isabel. Isabel and her family were here last summer. Muriel's out west."

"I meant Isabel."

Shortly after this the old lady falls asleep, her head on the side, her mouth open. "Excuse her manners," Nora says. "It's old age." She fixes an afghan over her mother and says we can all go into the front room where our talking won't disturb her.

"You two," my father says. "Do you want to go outside and amuse yourselves?"

Amuse ourselves how? Anyway I want to stay. The front room is more interesting than the kitchen, though barer. There is a gramophone and a pump organ and a picture on the wall of Mary, Jesus' mother—I know that much—in shades of bright blue and pink with a spiked band of light around her head. I know that such pictures are found only in the homes of Roman Catholics and so Nora must be one. We have never known any Roman Catholics at all well, never well enough to visit in their houses. I think of what my grandmother and my Aunt Tena, over in Dungannon, used to always say to indicate that somebody was a Catholic. *So-and-so digs with the wrong foot*, they would say. *She digs with the wrong foot*. That was what they would say about Nora.

Nora takes a bottle, half full, out of the top of the organ and pours some of what is in it into the two glasses that she and my father have emptied of the orange drink.

"Keep it in case of sickness?" my father says.

"Not on your life," says Nora. "I'm never sick. I just keep it because I keep it. One bottle does me a fair time, though, because I don't care for drinking alone. Here's luck!" She and my father drink and I know what it is. Whisky. One of the things my mother has told me in our talks together is that my father never drinks whisky. But I see he does. He drinks whisky and he talks of people whose names I have never heard before. But after a while he turns to a familiar incident. He tells about the chamberpot that was emptied out the window. "Picture me there," he says, "hollering my heartiest. *Oh, lady, it's your Walker Brothers man, anybody home?*" He does himself hollering, grinning absurdly, waiting, looking up in pleased expectation and then—oh, ducking, covering his head with his arms, looking as if he begged for mercy (when he never did anything like that, I was watching), and Nora laughs, almost as hard as my brother did at the time.

"That isn't true! That's not a word true!"

"Oh, indeed it is ma'am. We have our heroes in the ranks of Walker Brothers. I'm glad you think it's funny," he says sombrely.

I ask him shyly, "Sing the song."

"What song? Have you turned into a singer on top of everything else?"

Embarrassed, my father says, "Oh, just this song I made up while I was driving around, it gives me something to do, making up rhymes."

But after some urging he does sing it, looking at Nora with a droll, apologetic expression, and she laughs so much that in places he has to stop and wait for her to get over laughing so he can go on, because she makes him laugh too. Then he does various parts of his salesman's spiel. Nora when she laughs squeezes her large bosom under her folded arms. "You're crazy," she says. "That's all you are." She sees my brother peering into the gramophone and she jumps up and goes over to him. "Here's us sitting enjoying ourselves and not giving you a thought, isn't it terrible?" she says. "You want me to put a record on, don't you? You want to hear a nice record? Can you dance? I bet your sister can, can't she?"

I say no. "A big girl like you and so good-looking and can't dance!" says Nora. "It's high time you learned. I bet you'd make a lovely dancer. Here, I'm going to put on a piece I used to dance to and even your daddy did, in his dancing days. You didn't know your daddy was a dancer, did you? Well, he is a talented man, your daddy!"

She puts down the lid and takes hold of me unexpectedly around the waist, picks up my other hand and starts making me go backwards. "This is the way, now, this is how they dance. Follow me. This foot, see. One and one-two. One and one-two. That's fine, that's lovely, don't look at your feet! Follow me, that's right, see how easy? You're going to be a lovely dancer! One and one-two. One and one-two. Ben, see your daughter dancing!" *Whispering while you cuddle near me Whispering where no one can hear me....*

Round and round the linoleum, me proud, intent, Nora laughing and moving with great buoyancy, wrapping me in her strange gaiety, her smell of whisky, cologne, and sweat. Under the arms her dress is damp, and little drops form along her upper lip, hang in the soft black hairs at the corners of her mouth. She whirls me around in front of my father—causing me to stumble, for I am by no means so swift a pupil as she pretends—and lets me go, breathless.

"Dance with me, Ben."

"I'm the world's worst dancer, Nora, and you know it."

"I certainly never thought so."

"You would now."

She stands in front of him, arms hanging loose and hopeful, her breasts, which a moment ago embarrassed me with their warmth and bulk, rising and falling under her loose flowered dress, her face shining with the exercise, and delight.

"Ben."

My father drops his head and says quietly, "Not me, Nora."

So she can only go and take the record off. "I can drink alone but I can't dance alone," she says. "Unless I am a whole lot crazier than I think I am."

"Nora," says my father smiling. "You're not crazy."

"Stay for supper."

"Oh, no. We couldn't put you to the trouble."

"It's no trouble. I'd be glad of it."

"And their mother would worry. She'd think I'd turned us over in a ditch."

"Oh, well. Yes."

"We've taken a lot of your time now."

"Time," says Nora bitterly. "Will you come by ever again?"

"I will if I can," says my father.

"Bring the children. Bring your wife."

"Yes I will," says my father. "I will if I can."

When she follows us to the car he says, "You come to see us too, Nora. We're right on Grove Street, left-hand side going in, that's north, and two doors this side—east—of Baker Street."

Nora does not repeat these directions. She stands close to the car in her soft, brilliant dress. She touches the fender, making an unintelligible mark in the dust there.

On the way home my father does not buy any ice cream or pop, but he does go into a country store and get a package of licorice, which he shares with us. *She digs with the wrong foot*, I think, and the words seem sad to me as never before, dark, perverse. My father does not say anything to me about not mentioning things at home, but I know, just from the thoughtfulness, the pause when he passes the licorice, that there are things not to be mentioned. The whisky, maybe the dancing. No worry about my brother, he does not notice enough. At most he might remember the blind lady, the picture of Mary.

"Sing," my brother commands my father, but my father says gravely, "I don't know, I seem to be fresh out of songs. You watch the road and let me know if you see any rabbits."

So my father drives and my brother watches the road for rabbits and I feel my father's life flowing back from our car in the last of the afternoon, darkening and turning strange, like a landscape that has an enchantment on it, making it kindly, ordinary and familiar while you are looking at it, but changing it, once your back is turned, into something you will never know, with all kinds of weathers, and distances you cannot imagine.

When we get closer to Tuppertown the sky becomes gently overcast, as always, nearly always, on summer evenings by the Lake.

One's a Heifer

My uncle was laid up that winter with sciatica, so when the blizzard stopped and still two of the yearlings hadn't come home with the other cattle, Aunt Ellen said I'd better saddle Tim and start out looking for them.

"Then maybe I'll not be back tonight," I told her firmly. "Likely they've drifted as far as the sandhills. There's no use coming home without them."

I was thirteen, and had never been away like that all night before, but, busy with the breakfast, Aunt Ellen said yes, that sounded sensible enough, and while I ate, hunted up a dollar in silver for my meals.

"Most people wouldn't take it from a lad, but they're strangers up towards the hills. Bring it out independent-like, but don't insist too much. They're more likely to grudge you a feed of oats for Tim."

After breakfast I had to undress again, and put on two suits of underwear and two pairs of thick, home-knitted stockings. It was a clear, bitter morning. After the storm the drifts lay clean and unbroken to the horizon. Distant

SINCLAIR
ROSS

farm-buildings stood out distinct against the prairie as if the thin sharp atmosphere were a magnifying glass. As I started off Aunt Ellen peered cautiously out of the door a moment through a cloud of steam, and waved a red and white checkered dish-towel. I didn't wave back, but conscious of her uneasiness rode erect, as jaunty as the sheepskin and two suits of underwear would permit.

We took the road straight south about three miles. The calves, I reasoned, would have by this time found their way home if the blizzard hadn't carried them at least that far. Then we started catercornering across fields, riding over to straw-stacks where we could see cattle sheltering, calling at farmhouses to ask had they seen any strays. "Yearlings," I said each time politely. "Red with white spots and faces. The same almost except that one's a heifer and the other isn't."

Nobody had seen them. There was a crust on the snow not quite hard enough to carry Tim, and despite the cold his flanks and shoulders soon were steaming. He walked with his head down, and sometimes, taking my sympathy for granted, drew up a minute for breath.

My spirits, too, began to flag. The deadly cold and the flat white silent miles of prairie asserted themselves like a disapproving presence. The cattle round the straw-stacks stared when we rode up as if we were intruders. The fields stared, and the sky stared. People shivered in their doorways, and said they'd seen no strays.

At about one o'clock we stopped at a farmhouse for dinner. It was a single oat sheaf half thistles for Tim, and fried eggs and bread and tea for me. Crops had been poor that year, they apologized, and though they shook their heads when I brought out my money I saw the woman's eyes light greedily a second as if her instincts of hospitality were struggling hard against some urgent need. We too, I said, had had poor crops lately. That was why it was so important that I find the calves.

We rested an hour, then went on again. "Yearlings," I

kept on describing them. "Red with white spots and faces. The same except that one's a heifer and the other isn't."

Still no one had seen them, still it was cold, still Tim protested what a fool I was.

The country began to roll a little. A few miles ahead I could see the first low line of sandhills. "They'll be there for sure," I said aloud, more to encourage myself than Tim. "Keeping straight to the road it won't take a quarter as long to get home again."

But home now seemed a long way off. A thin white sheet of cloud spread across the sky, and though there had been no warmth in the sun the fields looked colder and bleaker without the glitter on the snow. Straw-stacks were fewer here, as if the land were poor, and every house we stopped at seemed more dilapidated than the one before.

A nagging wind rose as the afternoon wore on. Dogs yelped and bayed at us, and sometimes from the hills, like the signal of our approach, there was a thin, wavering howl of a coyote. I began to dread the miles home again almost as much as those still ahead. There were so many cattle straggling across the fields, so many yearlings just like ours. I saw them for sure a dozen times, and as often choked my disappointment down and clicked Tim on again.

2

And at last I really saw them. It was nearly dusk, and along with fifteen or twenty other cattle they were making their way towards some buildings that lay huddled at the foot of the sandhills. They passed in single file less than fifty yards away, but when I pricked Tim forward to turn them back he floundered in a snowed-in water-cut. By the time we were out they were a little distance ahead, and on account of the drifts it was impossible to put on a spurt of speed and pass them. All we could do was take our place at the end of the file, and proceed at their pace towards the buildings.

It was about half a mile. As we drew near I debated with Tim whether we should ask to spend the night or start off right away for home. We were hungry and tired, but it was a poor, shiftless-looking place. The yard was littered with old wagons and machinery; the house was scarcely distinguishable from the stables. Darkness was beginning to close in, but there was no light in the windows.

Then as we crossed the yard we heard a shout, "Stay where you are," and a man came running towards us from the stable. He was tall and ungainly, and, instead of the short sheepskin that most farmers wear, had on a long black overcoat nearly to his feet. He seized Tim's bridle when he reached us, and glared for a minute as if he were going to pull me out of the saddle. "I told you to stay out," he said in a harsh, excited voice. "You heard me, didn't you? What do you want coming round here anyway?"

I steeled myself and said, "Our two calves."

The muscles of his face were drawn together threateningly, but close to him like this and looking straight into his eyes I felt that for all their fierce look there was something about them wavering and uneasy. "The two red ones with the white faces," I continued. "They've just gone into the shed over there with yours. If you'll give me a hand getting them out again I'll start for home now right away."

He peered at me a minute, let go the bridle, then clutched it again. "They're all mine," he countered. "I was over by the gate. I watched them coming in."

His voice was harsh and thick. The strange wavering look in his eyes steadied itself for a minute to a dare. I forced myself to meet it and insisted, "I saw them back a piece in the field.They're ours all right. Let me go over a minute and I'll show you."

With a crafty tilt of his head he leered, "You didn't see any calves. And now, if you know what's good for you, you'll be on your way."

"You're trying to steal them," I flared rashly. "I'll go home and get my uncle and the police after you—then you'll see whether they're our calves or not."

My threat seemed to impress him a little. With a shifty

glance in the direction of the stable he said, "All right, come along and look them over. Then maybe you'll be satisfied." But all the way across the yard he kept his hand on Tim's bridle, and at the shed made me wait a few minutes while he went inside.

The cattle shed was a lean-to on the horse stable. It was plain enough: he was hiding the calves before letting me inside to look around. While waiting for him, however, I had time to realize that he was a lot bigger and stronger than I was, and that it might be prudent just to keep my eyes open, and not give him too much insolence.

He reappeared carrying a smoky lantern. "All right," he said pleasantly enough, "Come in and look around. Will your horse stand, or do you want to tie him?"

We put Tim in an empty stall in the horse stable, then went through a narrow doorway with a bar across it to the cattle shed. Just as I expected, our calves weren't there. There were two red ones with white markings that he tried to make me believe were the ones I had seen, but, positive I hadn't been mistaken, I shook my head and glanced at the doorway we had just come through. It was narrow, but not too narrow. He read my expression and said, "You think they're in there. Come on, then, and look around."

The horse stable consisted of two rows of open stalls with a passage down the centre like an aisle. At the far end were two box-stalls, one with a sick colt in it, the other closed. They were both boarded up to the ceiling, so that you could see inside them only through the doors. Again he read my expression, and with a nod towards the closed one said, "It's just a kind of harness room now. Up till a year ago I kept a stallion."

But he spoke furtively, and seemed anxious to get me away from that end of the stable. His smoky lantern threw great swaying shadows over us; and the deep clefts and triangles of shadow on his face sent a little chill through me, and made me think what a dark and evil face it was.

I was afraid, but not too afraid. "If it's just a harness room," I said recklessly, "why not let me see inside? Then I'll be satisfied and believe you."

He wheeled at my question, and sidled over swiftly to the stall. He stood in front of the door, crouched down a little, the lantern in front of him like a shield. There was a sudden stillness through the stable as we faced each other. Behind the light from his lantern the darkness hovered vast and sinister. It seemed to hold its breath, to watch and listen. I felt a clutch of fear now at my throat, but I didn't move. My eyes were fixed on him so intently that he seemed to lose substance, to loom up close a moment, then recede. At last he disappeared completely, and there was only the lantern like a hard hypnotic eye.

It held me. It held me rooted, against my will. I wanted to run from the stable, but I wanted even more to see inside the stall. And yet I was afraid to see inside the stall. So afraid that it was a relief when at last he gave a shame-faced laugh and said, "There's a hole in the floor—that's why I keep the door closed. If you didn't know, you might step into it—twist your foot. That's what happened to one of my horses a while ago."

I nodded as if I believed him, and went back tractably to Tim. But regaining control of myself as I tried the saddle girths, beginning to feel that my fear had been unwarranted, I looked up and said, "It's ten miles home, and we've been riding hard all day. If we could stay a while—have something to eat, and then get started—"

The wavering light came into his eyes again. He held the lantern up to see me better, such a long, intent scrutiny that it seemed he must discover my designs. But he gave a nod finally, as if reassured, brought oats and hay for Tim, and suggested, companionably, "After supper we can have a game of checkers."

Then, as if I were a grown-up, he put out his hand and said, "My name is Arthur Vickers."

3

Inside the house, rid of his hat and coat, he looked less forbidding. He had a white nervous face, thin lips, a large straight nose, and deep uneasy eyes. When the lamp was lit I fancied I could still see the wavering expression in them, and decided it was what you called a guilty look.

"You won't think much of it," he said apologetically, following my glance around the room. "I ought to be getting things cleaned up again. Come over to the stove. Supper won't take long."

It was a large, low-ceilinged room that for the first moment or two struck me more like a shed or granary than a house. The table in the centre was littered with tools and harness. On a rusty cook-stove were two big steaming pots of bran. Next to the stove stood a grindstone, then a white iron bed covered with coats and horse blankets. At the end opposite the bed, weasel and coyote skins were drying. There were guns and traps on the wall, a horse collar, a pair of rubber boots. The floor was bare and grimy. Ashes were littered around the stove. In a corner squatted a live owl with a broken wing.

He walked back and forth a few times looking helplessly at the disorder, then cleared off the table and lifted the pots of bran to the back of the stove. "I've been mending harness," he explained. "You get careless, living alone like this. It takes a woman anyway."

My presence, apparently, was making him take stock of the room. He picked up a broom and swept for a minute, made an ineffective attempt to straighten the blankets on the bed, brought another lamp out of a cupboard and lit it. There was an ungainly haste to all his movements. He started unbuckling my sheepskin for me, then turned away suddenly to take off his own coat. "Now we'll have supper," he said with an effort at self-possession. "Coffee and beans is all I can give you—maybe a little molasses."

I replied diplomatically that that sounded pretty good. It

didn't seem right, accepting hospitality this way from a man who was trying to steal your calves, but theft, I reflected, surely justified deceit. I held my hands out to the warmth, and asked if I could help.

There was a kettle of plain navy beans already cooked. He dipped out enough for our supper into a frying pan, and on top laid rashers of fat salt pork. While I watched that they didn't burn he rinsed off a few dishes. Then he set out sugar and canned milk, butter, molasses, and dark heavy biscuits that he had baked himself the day before. He kept glancing at me so apologetically all the while that I leaned over and sniffed the beans, and said at home I ate a lot of them.

"It takes a woman," he repeated as we sat down to the table. "I don't often have anyone here to eat with me. If I'd known, I'd have cleaned things up a little."

I was too intent on my plateful of beans to answer. All through the meal he sat watching me, but made no further attempts at conversation. Hungry as I was, I noticed that the wavering, uneasy look was still in his eyes. A guilty look, I told myself again, and wondered what I was going to do to get the calves away. I finished my coffee and he continued:

"It's worse even than this in the summer. No time for meals—and the heat and flies. Last summer I had a girl cooking for a few weeks, but it didn't last. Just a cow she was —just a big stupid cow—and she wanted to stay on. There's a family of them back in the hills. I had to send her home."

I wondered should I suggest starting now, or ask to spend the night. Maybe when he's asleep, I thought, I can slip out of the house and get away with the calves. He went on, "You don't know how bad it is sometimes. Weeks on end and no one to talk to. You're not yourself—you're not sure what you're going to say or do."

I remembered hearing my uncle talk about a man who had gone crazy living alone. And this fellow Vickers had queer eyes all right. And there was the live owl over in the corner, and the grindstone standing right beside the bed. "Maybe I'd better go now," I decided aloud. "Tim'll be rested, and it's ten miles home."

But he said no, it was colder now, with the wind getting stronger, and seemed so kindly and concerned that I half forgot my fears. "Likely he's just starting to go crazy," I told myself, "And it's only by staying that I'll have a chance to get the calves away."

When the table was cleared and the dishes washed he said he would go out and bed down the stable for the night. I picked up my sheepskin to go with him, but he told me sharply to stay inside. Just for a minute he looked crafty and forbidding as when I first rode up on Tim, and to allay his suspicions I nodded compliantly and put my sheepskin down again. It was better like that anyway, I decided. In a few minutes I could follow him, and perhaps, taking advantage of the shadows and his smoky lantern, make my way to the box-stall unobserved.

But when I reached the stable he had closed the door after him and hooked it from the inside. I walked round a while, tried to slip in by way of the cattle shed, and then had to go back to the house. I went with a vague feeling of relief again. There was still time, I told myself, and it would be safer anyway when he was sleeping.

So that it would be easier to keep from falling asleep myself I planned to suggest coffee again just before we went to bed. I knew that the guest didn't ordinarily suggest such things, but it was no time to remember manners when there was someone trying to steal your calves.

4

When he came in from the stable we played checkers. I was no match for him, but to encourage me he repeatedly let me win. "It's a long time now since I've had a chance to play," he kept on saying, trying to convince me that his short-sighted moves weren't intentional. "Sometimes I used to ask her to play, but I had to tell her every move to make.

If she didn't win she'd upset the board and go off and sulk."

"My aunt is a little like that too," I said. "She cheats sometimes when we're playing cribbage—and, when I catch her, says her eyes aren't good."

"Women talk too much ever to make good checker players. It takes concentration. This one, though, couldn't even talk like anybody else."

After my long day in the cold I was starting to yawn already. He noticed it, and spoke in a rapid, earnest voice, as if afraid I might lose interest soon and want to go to bed. It was important for me too to stay awake, so I crowned a king and said, "Why don't you get someone, then, to stay with you?"

"Too many of them want to do that." His face darkened a little, almost as if warning me. "Too many of the kind you'll never get rid of again. She did, last summer when she was here. I had to put her out."

There was silence for a minute, his eyes flashing, and wanting to placate him I suggested, "She liked you, maybe."

He laughed a moment, harshly. "She liked me all right. Just two weeks ago she came back—walked over with an old suitcase and said she was going to stay. It was cold at home, and she had to work too hard, and she didn't mind even if I couldn't pay her wages."

I was getting sleepier. To keep awake I sat on the edge of the chair where it was uncomfortable and said, "Hadn't you asked her to come?"

His eyes narrowed. "I'd had trouble enough getting rid of her the first time. There were six of them at home, and she said her father thought it time that someone married her."

"Then she must be a funny one," I said. "Everyone knows that the man's supposed to ask the girl."

My remark seemed to please him. "I told you, didn't I?" he said, straightening a little, jumping two of my men. "She was so stupid that at checkers she'd forget whether she was black or red."

We stopped playing now. I glanced at the owl in the corner and the ashes littered on the floor, and thought that keeping her would maybe have been a good idea after all. He read it in my face and said, "I used to think that too sometimes. I used to look at her and think nobody knew now anyway and that she'd maybe do. You need a woman on a farm all right. And night after night she'd be sitting there where you are—right there where you are, looking at me, not even trying to play—"

The fire was low, and we could hear the wind. "But then I'd go up in the hills, away from her for a while, and start thinking back the way things used to be, and it wasn't right even for the sake of your meals ready and your house kept clean. When she came back I tried to tell her that, but all the family are the same, and I realized it wasn't any use. There's nothing you can do when you're up against that sort of thing. The mother talks just like a child of ten. When she sees you coming she runs and hides. There are six of them, and it's come out in every one."

It was getting cold, but I couldn't bring myself to go over to the stove. There was the same stillness now as when he was standing at the box-stall door. And I felt the same illogical fear, the same powerlessness to move. It was the way his voice had lowered, the glassy, cold look in his eyes. The rest of his face disappeared; all I could see were his eyes. And they held me as the lantern had held me, held me intent, rigid, even as they filled me with a vague and over-powering dread. My voice gone a whisper on me I asked, "And when you wouldn't marry her—what happened then?"

He remained motionless a moment, as if answering silently; then with an unexpected laugh like a breaking dish said, "Why, nothing happened. I just told her she couldn't stay. I went to town for a few days—and when I came back she was gone."

"Has she been back to bother you since?" I asked.

He made a little silo of checkers. "No—she took her suitcase with her."

To remind him that the fire was going down I went over to the stove and stood warming myself. He raked the coals with the lifter and put in poplar, two split pieces for a base and a thick round log on top. I yawned again. He said maybe I'd like to go to bed now, and I shivered and asked him could I have a drink of coffee first. While it boiled he stood stirring the two big pots of bran. The trouble with coffee, I realized, was that it would keep him from getting sleepy too.

I undressed finally and got into bed, but he blew out only one of the lamps, and sat on playing checkers with himself. I dozed a while, then sat up with a start, afraid it was morning already and that I'd lost my chance to get the calves away. He came over and looked at me a minute, then gently pushed my shoulders back on the pillow. "Why don't you come to bed too?" I asked, and he said, "Later I will—I don't feel sleepy yet."

It was like that all night. I kept dozing on and off, wakening in a fright each time to find him still there sitting at his checker board. He would raise his head sharply when I stirred, then tiptoe over to the bed and stand close to me listening till satisfied again I was asleep. The owl kept wakening too. It was down in the corner still where the lamplight scarcely reached, and I could see its eyes go on and off like yellow bulbs. The wind whistled drearily around the house. The blankets smelled like an old granary. He suspected what I was planning to do, evidently, and was staying awake to make sure I didn't get outside.

Each time I dozed I dreamed I was on Tim again. The calves were in sight, but far ahead of us, and with the drifts so deep we couldn't overtake them. Then instead of Tim it was the grindstone I was straddling, and that was the reason, not the drifts, that we weren't making better progress.

I wondered what would happen to the calves if I didn't get away with them. My uncle had sciatica, and it would be at least a day before I could be home and back again with some of the neighbors. By then Vickers might have butchered the calves, or driven them up to a hiding place in the hills where we'd never find them. There was the possibility, too, that Aunt Ellen and the neighbors wouldn't believe me. I dozed and woke—dozed and woke—always he was sitting at the checker board. I could hear the dry tinny ticking of an alarm clock, but from where I was lying couldn't see it. He seemed to be listening to it too. The wind would sometimes creak the house, and then he would give a start and sit rigid a moment with his eyes fixed on the window. It was the window, as if there was nothing he was afraid of that could reach him by the door.

Most of the time he played checkers with himself, moving his lips, muttering words I couldn't hear, but once I woke to find him staring fixedly across the table as if he had a partner sitting there. His hands were clenched in front of him, there was a sharp, metallic glitter in his eyes. I lay transfixed, unbreathing. His eyes as I watched seemed to dilate, to brighten, to harden like a bird's. For a long time he sat contracted, motionless, as if gathering himself to strike, then furtively he slid his hand an inch or two along the table towards some checkers that were piled beside the board. It was as if he were reaching for a weapon, as if his invisible partner were an enemy. He clutched the checkers, slipped slowly from his chair and straightened. His movements were sure, stealthy, silent like a cat's. His face had taken on a desperate, contorted look. As he raised his hand the tension was unbearable.

It was a long time—a long time watching him the way you watch a finger tightening slowly on the trigger of a gun —and then suddenly wrenching himself to action he hurled the checkers with such vicious fury that they struck the wall in front of him and clattered back across the room.

And then everything was quiet again. I started a little, mumbled to myself as if half-awakened, lay quite still. But he seemed to have forgotten me, and after standing limp and dazed a minute got down on his knees and started looking for the checkers. When he had them all, he put more wood in the stove, then returned quietly to the table and sat down. We were alone again; everything was exactly as before. I relaxed gradually, telling myself that he'd just been seeing things.

The next time I woke he was sitting with his head sunk forward on the table. It looked as if he had fallen asleep at last, and huddling alert among the bed-clothes I decided to watch a minute to make sure, then dress and try to slip out to the stable.

While I watched, I planned exactly every movement I was going to make. Rehearsing it in my mind as carefully as if I were actually doing it, I climbed out of bed, put on my clothes, tiptoed stealthily to the door and slipped outside. By this time, though, I was getting drowsy, and relaxing among the blankets I decided that for safety's sake I should rehearse it still again. I rehearsed it four times altogether, and the fourth time dreamed that I hurried on successfully to the stable.

I fumbled with the door a while, then went inside and felt my way through the darkness to the box-stall. There was a bright light suddenly and the owl was sitting over the door with his yellow eyes like a pair of lanterns. The calves, he told me, were in the other stall with the sick colt. I looked and they were there all right, but Tim came up and said it might be better not to start for home till morning. He reminded me that I hadn't paid for his feed or my own supper yet, and that if I slipped off this way it would mean that I was stealing too. I agreed, realizing now that it wasn't the calves I was looking for after all, and that I still had to see inside the stall that was guarded by the owl. "Wait here," Tim said, "I'll tell you if he flies away," and without further questioning I lay down in the straw and went to sleep again. . . . When I woke coffee and beans were on the stove already, and though the lamp was still lit I could tell by the window that it was nearly morning.

5

We were silent during breakfast. Two or three times I caught him watching me, and it seemed his eyes were shiftier than before. After his sleepless night he looked tired and haggard. He left the table while I was still eating and fed raw rabbit to the owl, then came back and drank another cup of coffee. He had been friendly and communicative the night before, but now, just as when he first came running out of the stable in his long black coat, his expression was sullen and resentful. I began to feel that he was in a hurry to be rid of me.

I took my time, however, racking my brains to outwit him still and get the calves away. It looked pretty hopeless now, his eyes on me so suspiciously, my imagination at low ebb. Even if I did get inside the box-stall to see the calves—was he going to stand back then and let me start off home with them? Might it not more likely frighten him, make him do something desperate, so that I couldn't reach my uncle or the police? There was the owl over in the corner, the grindstone by the bed. And with such a queer fellow you could never tell. You could never tell, and you had to think about your own skin too. So I said politely, "Thank you, Mr. Vickers, for letting me stay all night," and remembering what Tim had told me took out my dollar's worth of silver.

He gave a short dry laugh and wouldn't take it. "Maybe you'll come back," he said, "and next time stay longer. We'll go shooting up in the hills if you like—and I'll make a trip to town for things so that we can have better meals. You need company sometimes for a change. There's been no one here now quite a while."

His face softened again as he spoke. There was an expression in his eyes as if he wished that I could stay on now. It puzzled me. I wanted to be indignant, and it was impossible. He held my sheepskin for me while I put it on, and tied the scarf around the collar with a solicitude and determination equal to Aunt Ellen's. And then he gave his short dry laugh again, and hoped I'd find my calves all right.

He had been out to the stable before I was awake, and Tim was ready for me, fed and saddled. But I delayed a few minutes, pretending to be interested in his horses and the sick colt. It would be worth something after all, I realized, to get just a glimpse of the calves. Aunt Ellen was going to be sceptical enough of my story as it was. It could only confirm her doubts to hear me say I hadn't seen the calves in the box-stall, and was just pretty sure that they were there.

So I went from stall to stall, stroking the horses and making comparisons with the ones we had at home. The door, I noticed, he had left wide open, ready for me to lead out Tim. He was walking up and down the aisle, telling me which horses were quiet, which to be careful of. I came to a nervous chestnut mare, and realized she was my only chance.

She crushed her hips against the side of the stall as I slipped up to her manger, almost pinning me, then gave her head a toss and pulled back hard on the halter shank. The shank, I noticed, was tied with an easy slip-knot that the right twist and a sharp tug would undo in half a second. And the door was wide open, ready for me to lead out Tim—and standing as she was with her body across the stall diagonally, I was for the moment screened from sight.

It happened quickly. There wasn't time to think of consequences. I just pulled the knot, in the same instant struck the mare across the nose. With a snort she threw herself backwards, almost trampling Vickers, then flung up her head to keep from tripping on the shank and plunged outside.

It worked as I hoped it would. "Quick," Vickers yelled to me, "the gate's open—try and head her off"—but instead I just waited till he himself was gone, then fairly flew to the box-stall.

The door was fastened with two tight-fitting slide-bolts, one so high that I could scarcely reach it standing on my toes. It wouldn't yield. There was a piece of broken whiffle-tree beside the other box-stall door. I snatched it up and started hammering on the pin. Still it wouldn't yield. The head of the pin was small and round, and the whiffle-tree kept glancing off. I was too terrified to pause a moment and take careful aim.

Terrified of the stall though, not of Vickers. Terrified of the stall, yet compelled by a frantic need to get inside. For the moment I had forgotten Vickers, forgotten even the danger of his catching me. I worked blindly, helplessly, as if I were confined and smothering. For a moment I yielded to panic, dropped the piece of whiffle-tree and started kicking at the door. Then, collected again, I forced back the lower bolt, and picking up the whiffle-tree tried to pry the door out a little at the bottom. But I had wasted too much time. Just as I dropped to my knees to peer through the opening Vickers seized me. I struggled to my feet and fought a moment, but it was such a hard, strangling clutch at my throat that I felt myself go limp and blind. In desperation then I kicked him, and with a blow like a reflex he sent me staggering to the floor.

But it wasn't the blow that frightened me. It was the fierce, wild light in his eyes.

Stunned as I was, I looked up and saw him watching me, and, sick with terror, made a bolt for Tim. I untied him with hands that moved incredibly, galvanized for escape. I knew now for sure that Vickers was crazy. He followed me outside, and just as I mounted; seized Tim again by the bridle. For a second or two it made me crazy too. Gathering up the free ends of the reins I lashed him hard across the face. He let go of the bridle, and, frightened and excited too now, Tim made a dash across the yard and out of the gate. Deep as the snow was, I kept him galloping for half a mile, pommelling him with my fists, kicking my heels against his sides. Then of his own accord he drew up short for breath, and I looked around to see whether Vickers was following. He wasn't—there was only the snow and the hills, his buildings a lonely little smudge against the whiteness—and the relief was like a stick pulled out that's been holding up tomato vines or peas.

I slumped across the saddle weakly, and till Tim started on again lay there whimpering like a baby.

6

We were home by noon. We didn't have to cross fields or stop at houses now, and there had been teams on the road packing down the snow so that Tim could trot part of the way and even canter. I put him in the stable without taking time to tie or unbridle him, and ran to the house to tell Aunt Ellen. But I was still frightened, cold and a little hysterical, and it was a while before she could understand how everything had happened. She was silent a minute, indulgent, then helping me off with my sheepskin said kindly, "You'd better forget about it now, and come over and get warm. The calves came home themselves yesterday. Just about an hour after you set out."

I looked up at her. "But the stall, then—just because I wanted to look inside he knocked me down—and if it wasn't the calves in there—"

She didn't answer. She was busy building up the fire and looking at the stew.

The Move

I have perhaps never envied anyone as much as a girl I knew when I was about eleven years old and of whom today I remember not much more than the name, Florence. Her father was a mover. I don't think this was his trade. He was a handyman, I imagine, engaging in various odd jobs; at the time of the seasonal movings—and it seems to me that people changed their lodgings often in those days—he moved the household effects of people of small means who lived near us and even quite far away, in the suburbs and distant quarters of Winnipeg. No doubt, his huge cart and his horses, which he had not wanted to dispose of when he came from the country to the city, had made him a mover.

On Saturdays Florence accompanied her father on his journeys, which, because of the slow pace of the horses, often took the entire day. I envied her to the point of having no more than one fixed idea: Why was my father not also a mover? What finer trade could one practice?

GABRIELLE
ROY

I don't know what moving signified to me in those days. Certainly I could

132

not have had any clear idea what it was like. I had been born and had grown up in the fine, comfortable house in which we were still living and which, in all probability, we would never leave. Such fixity seemed frightfully monotonous to me that summer. Actually we were never really away from that large house. If we were going to the country for a while, even if we were only to be absent for a day, the problem immediately arose: Yes, but who will look after the house?

To take one's furniture and belongings, to abandon a place, close a door behind one forever, say good-by to a neighborhood, this was an adventure of which I knew nothing; and it was probably the sheer force of my efforts to picture it to myself that made it seem so daring, heroic, and exalted in my eyes.

"Aren't we ever going to move?" I used to ask Maman.

"I certainly hope not," she would say. "By the grace of God and the long patience of your father, we are solidly established at last. I only hope it is forever."

She told me that to her no sight in the world could be more heartbreaking, more poignant even, than a house moving.

"For a while," she said, "it's as if you were related to the nomads, those poor souls who slip along the surface of existence, putting their roots down nowhere. You no longer have a roof over your head. Yes indeed, for a few hours at least, it's as if you were drifting on the stream of life."

Poor Mother! Her objections and comparisons only strengthened my strange hankering. To drift on the stream of life! To be like the nomads! To wander through the world! There was nothing in any of this that did not seem to me complete felicity.

Since I myself could not move, I wished to be present at someone else's moving and see what it was all about. Summer came. My unreasonable desire grew. Even now I cannot speak of it lightly, much less so with derision. Certain of our desires, as if they knew about us before we do ourselves, do not deserve to be mocked.

Each Saturday morning I used to go and wander around Florence's house. Her father—a big dirty-blond man in blue work clothes, always grumbling a little or even, perhaps, swearing—would be busy getting the impressive cart out of the barn. When the horses were harnessed and provided with nose bags of oats, the father and his little daughter would climb onto the high seat; the father would take the reins in his hands; they would both, it seemed to me, look at me then with slight pity, a vague commiseration. I would feel forsaken, of an inferior species of humans unworthy of high adventure.

The father would shout something to the horses. The cart would shake. I would watch them set out in that cool little morning haze that seems to promise such delightful emotions to come. I would wave my hand at them, even though they never looked back at me. "Have a good trip," I would call. I would feel so unhappy at being left behind that I would nurse my regret all day and with it an aching curiosity. What would they see today? Where were they at this moment? What was offering itself to their travelers' eyes? It was no use my knowing that they could go only a limited distance in any event. I would imagine the two of them seeing things that no one else in the world could see. From the top of the cart, I thought, how transformed the world must appear.

At last my desire to go with them was so strong and so constant that I decided to ask my mother for permission—although I was almost certain I would never obtain it. She held my new friends in rather poor esteem and, though she tolerated my hanging continually about them, smelling their odor of horses, adventure, and dust, I knew in my heart of hearts that the mere idea that I might wish to accompany them would fill her with indignation.

At my first words, indeed, she silenced me.

"Are you mad? To wander about the city in a moving

wagon! Just picture yourself," she said, "in the midst of
furniture and boxes and piled-up mattresses all day, and with
who knows what people! What can you imagine would be
pleasant about that?"

How strange it was. Even the idea, for instance, of being
surrounded by heaped-up chairs, chests with empty drawers,
unhooked pictures—the very novelty of all this stimulated
my desire.

"Never speak of that whim to me again," said my mother.
"The answer is no and no it will remain."

Next day I went over to see Florence, to feed my nostalgic
envy of their existence on the few words she might say to
me.

"Where did you go yesterday? Who did you move?"

"Oh I'm not sure," Florence said, chewing gum—she was
always either chewing gum or sucking a candy. "We went
over to Fort Rouge, I think, to get some folks and move
them way to hell and gone over by East Kildonan."

These were the names of quite ordinary suburbs. Why
was it that at moments such as these they seemed to hold the
slightly poignant attraction of those parts of the world that
are remote, mysterious, and difficult to reach?

"What did you see?" I asked.

Florence shifted her gum from one cheek to the other,
looking at me with slightly foolish eyes. She was not an
imaginative child. No doubt, to her and her father, the
latter's work seemed banal, dirty, and tiring, and nothing
more similar to one household move than another household move. Later I discovered that if Florence accompanied
her father every Saturday, it was only because her mother
went out cleaning that day and there was no one to look
after the little girl at home. So her father took her along.

Both father and daughter began to consider me a trifle
mad to endow their life with so much glamour.

I had asked the big pale-blond man countless times if he
wouldn't take me too. He always looked at me for a moment
as at some sort of curiosity—a child who perhaps wasn't

completely normal—and said, "If your mother gives you permission . . ." and spat on the ground, hitched up his huge trousers with a movement of his hips, then went off to feed his horses or grease the wheels of his cart.

The end of the moving season was approaching. In the blazing heat of summer no one moved except people who were being evicted or who had to move closer to a new job, rare cases. If I don't soon manage to see what moving is like, I thought, I'll have to wait till next summer. And who knows? Next summer I may no longer have such a taste for it.

The notion that my desire might not always mean so much to me, instead of cheering me, filled me with anxiety. I began to realize that even our desires are not eternally faithful to us, that they wear out, perhaps die, or are replaced by others, and this precariousness of their lives made them seem more touching to me, more friendly. I thought that if we do not satisfy them they must go away somewhere and perish of boredom and lassitude.

Observing that I was still taken up with my "whim," Maman perhaps thought she might distract me from it by telling me once more the charming stories of her own childhood. She chose, oddly enough, to tell me again about the long journey of her family across the prairie by covered wagon. The truth must have been that she herself relived this thrilling voyage into the unknown again and again and that, by recounting it to me, she perhaps drained away some of that heartbreaking nostalgia that our life deposits in us, whatever it may be.

So here she was telling me again how, crowded together in the wagon—for Grandmother had brought some of her furniture, her spinning wheel certainly, and innumerable bundles—pressed closely in together, they had journeyed across the immense country.

"The prairie at that time," she said, "seemed even more immense than it does today, for there were no villages to speak of along the trail and only a few houses. To see even one, away far off in the distance, was an adventure in itself."

"And what did you feel?" I asked her.

"I was attracted," Maman admitted, bowing her head slightly, as if there were something a bit wrong, or at least strange, about this. "Attracted by the space, the great bare sky, the way the tiniest tree was visible in this solitude for miles. I was very much attracted."

"So you were happy?"

"Happy? Yes, I think so. Happy without knowing why. Happy as you are, when you are young—or even not so young—simply because you are in motion, because life is changing and will continue to change and everything is being renewed. It's curious," she told me. "Such things must run in families, for I wonder whether there have ever been such born travelers as all of us."

And she promised me that later on I too would know what it is to set forth, to be always seeking from life a possible beginning over—and that perhaps I might even become weary of it.

That night the intensity of my desire wakened me from sleep. I imagined myself in my mother's place, a child lying, as she had described it, on the floor of the wagon, watching the prairie stars—the most luminous stars in either hemisphere, it is said—as they journeyed over her head.

That, I thought, I shall never know; it is a life that is gone beyond recall and lost—and the mere fact that there were ways of life that were over, extinct in the past, and that we could not recover them in our day, filled me with the same nostalgic longing for the lost years as I had felt for my own perishable desires. But, for lack of anything better, there was the possible journey with our neighbors.

I knew—I guessed, rather—that, though we owe obedience to our parents, we owe it also to certain of our desires, those that are strangest, piercing, and too vast.

I remained awake. Tomorrow—this very day, rather—was a Saturday, moving day. I had resolved to go with the Pichettes.

Dawn appeared. Had I ever really seen it until now? I noticed that before the sky becomes clean and shining, it takes on an indecisive color, like badly washed laundry.

Now, the desire that was pushing me so violently, to the point of revolt, had no longer anything happy or even tempting about it. It was more like an order. Anguish weighed upon my heart. I wasn't even free now to say to myself, "Sleep. Forget all that." I had to go.

Is it the same anguish that has wakened me so many times in my life, wakens me still at dawn with the awareness of an imminent departure, sad sometimes, sometimes joyful, but almost always toward an unknown destination? Is it always the same departure that is involved?

When I judged the morning to be sufficiently advanced, I got up and combed my hair. Curiously enough, for this trip in a cart, I chose to put on my prettiest dress. "Might as well be hung for a sheep as a lamb," I said to myself, and left the house without a sound.

I arrived soon at the mover's. He was yawning on the threshold of the barn, stretching his arms in the early sun. He considered me suspiciously.

"Have you got permission?"

I swallowed my saliva rapidly. I nodded.

A little later Florence appeared, looking bad-tempered and sleepy.

She hitched herself up onto the seat beside us.

"Giddup!" cried the man.

And we set out in that cool morning hour that had promised me the transformation of the world and everything in it—and undoubtedly of myself.

2

And at first the journey kept its promise. We were passing through a city of sonorous and empty streets, over which we rolled with a great noise. All the houses seemed to be still asleep, bathed in a curious and peaceful atmosphere of withdrawal. I had never seen our little town wearing this absent, gentle air of remoteness.

The great rising sun bleached and purified it, I felt. I seemed to be traveling through an absolutely unknown city, remote and still to be explored. And yet I was astonished to recognize, as if vaguely, buildings, church spires, and street crossings that I must have seen somewhere before. But how could this be, since I had this morning left the world I had known and was entering into a new one?

Soon streetcars and a few automobiles began to move about. The sight of them looming upon the horizon and coming toward us gave me a vivid sense of the shifting of epochs.

What had these streetcars and automobiles come to do in our time, which was that of the cart? I asked myself with pleasure. When we reached Winnipeg and became involved in already heavy traffic, my sense of strangeness was so great that I believed I must be dreaming and clapped my hands.

Even at that time a horse-drawn cart must have been rare in the center of the city. So, at our side, everything was moving quickly and easily. We, with our cumbrous and reflective gait, passed like a slow, majestic film. I am the past, I am times gone by, I said to myself with fervor.

People stopped to watch us pass. I looked at them in turn, as if from far away. What did we have in common with this modern, noisy, agitated city? Increasingly, high in the cart, I became a survivor from times past. I had to restrain myself from beginning to salute the crowds, the streets, and the city, as if they were lucky to see us sweeping by.

For I had a tendency to divide into two people, actor and witness. From time to time I was the crowd that watched the passage of this astonishing cart from the past. Then I was the personage who considered from on high these modern times at her feet.

Meanwhile the difficulty of driving his somewhat nervous

horses through all this noise and traffic was making the mover, whom I would have expected to be calmer and more composed, increasingly edgy. He complained and even swore noisily at almost everything we encountered. This began to embarrass me. I felt that his bad temper was spoiling all the pleasure and the sense of gentle incongruity that the poor people of the present era might have obtained from our appearance in their midst. I should have very much liked to disassociate myself from him. But how could I, jammed in beside him as I was?

Finally, we took to small, quieter streets. I saw then that we were going toward Fort Garry.

"Is that the way we're going?"

"Yes," replied Monsieur Pichette ungraciously. "That's the way."

The heat was becoming overpowering. Without any shelter, wedged between the big bulky man and Florence, who made no effort to leave me a comfortable place, I was beginning to suffer greatly. At last, after several hours, we were almost in the country.

The houses were still ranked along narrow streets, but now these were short and beyond them the prairie could be seen like a great recumbent land—a land so widespread that doubtless one would never be able to see either its end or its beginning. My heart began once more to beat hard.

There begins the land of the prairies, I said to myself. There begins the infinite prairie of Canada.

"Are we going to go onto the real prairie?" I asked. "Or are we still really inside the city limits?"

"You are certainly the most inquisitive little girl I've ever seen in my life," grumbled Monsieur Pichette, and he told me nothing at all.

Now the roads were only of dirt, which the wind lifted in dusty whirlwinds. The houses spaced themselves out, became smaller and smaller. Finally they were no more than badly constructed shacks, put together out of various odds and ends—a bit of tin, a few planks, some painted, some raw —and they all seemed to have been raised during the night only to be demolished the next day. Yet, unfinished as they were, the little houses still seemed old. Before one of them we stopped.

The people had begun to pile up their belongings, in the house or outside it, in cardboard cartons or merely thrown pell-mell into bedcovers with the corners knotted to form rough bundles. But they were not very far along, according to Monsieur Pichette, who flew into a rage the moment we arrived.

"I only charge five dollars to move people," he said, "and they aren't even ready when I get here."

We all began to transport the household effects from the shack to the cart. I joined in, carrying numerous small objects that fell to my hand—saucepans with unmatching covers, a pot, a chipped water jug. I was trying, I think, to distract myself, to keep, if at all possible, the little happiness I had left. For I was beginning to realize that the adventure was taking a sordid turn. In this poor, exhausted-looking woman with her hair plastered to her face, and in her husband—a man as lacking in amiability as Monsieur Pichette—I was discovering people who were doomed to a life of which I knew nothing, terribly gray and, it seemed to me, without exit. So I tried to help them as much as I could and took it upon myself to carry some rather large objects on my own. At last I was told to sit still because I was getting in everyone's way.

I went to rejoin Florence, who was sitting a short distance away on a little wooden fence.

"Is it always like this?" I asked.

"Yes, like this—or worse."

"It's possible to be worse?"

"Much worse. These people," she said, "have beds, and dressers. . . ."

She refused to enlighten me further.

"I'm hungry," she decided and she ran to unpack a little lunch box, took out some bread and butter and an apple and proceeded to eat under my nose.

"Didn't you bring anything to eat?" she asked.

"No."

"You should have," she said, and continued to bite hungrily into her bread, without offering me a scrap.

I watched the men bring out some soiled mattresses, which they carried at arm's length. New mattresses are not too distressing a sight; but once they have become the slightest bit worn or dirty I doubt that any household object is more repugnant. Then the men carried out an old torn sofa on their shoulders, some bedposts and springs. I tried to whip up my enthusiasm, to revive a few flames of it, at least. And it was then, I think, that I had a consoling idea: we had come to remove these people from this wretched life; we were going to take them now to something better; we were going to find them a fine, clean house.

A little dog circled around us, whimpering, starving, perhaps anxious. For his sake more than my own maybe, I would have liked to obtain a few bits of Florence's lunch.

"Won't you give him a little bit?" I asked.

Florence hastily devoured a large mouthful.

"Let him try and get it," she said.

The cart was full now and, on the ground beside it, almost as many old things still waited to be stowed away.

I began to suffer for the horses, which would have all this to pull.

The house was completely emptied, except for bits of broken dishes and some absolutely worthless rags. The woman was the last to come out. This was the moment I had imagined as dramatic, almost historic, undoubtedly marked by some memorable gesture or word. But this poor creature, so weary and dust-covered, had apparently no regret at crossing her threshold, at leaving behind her two, three, or perhaps four years of her life.

"Come, we'll have to hurry," she said simply, "if we want to be in our new place before night."

She climbed onto the seat of the cart with one of the younger children, whom she took on her knees. The others went off with their father, to go a little way on foot, then by streetcar, to be ahead of us, they said, at the place where we were going.

Florence and I had to stand among the furniture piled up behind.

The enormous cart now looked like some sort of monster, with tubs and pails bouncing about on both sides, upturned chairs, huge clumsy packages bulging in all directions.

The horses pulled vigorously. We set out. Then the little dog began to run along behind us, whimpering so loudly in fear and despair that I cried, imagining that no one had thought of him, "We've forgotten the little dog. Stop. Wait for the little dog."

In the face of everyone's indifference, I asked the woman, whose name was Mrs. Smith, "Isn't he yours?"

"Yes, he's ours, I suppose," she replied.

"He's coming. Wait for him," I begged.

"Don't you think we're loaded up enough already?" the mover snapped dryly, and he whipped his horses.

For a long moment more the little dog ran along behind us.

He wasn't made for running, this little dog. His legs were too short and bowed. But he did his best. Ah yes! He did his best.

Is he going to try to follow us across the whole city? I thought with distress. Awkward, distracted, and upset as he was, he would surely be crushed by an automobile or a streetcar. I don't know which I dreaded most: to see him turn back alone toward the deserted house or try to cross the city, come what might. We were already turning onto a street that was furrowed with tracks. A streetcar was approaching in the distance; several cars passed us, honking.

Mrs. Smith leaned down from the seat of the cart and shouted at the little dog, "Go on home."

Then she repeated, more loudly, "Go on home, stupid."

So he had a sort of name, even though cruel, yet he was being abandoned.

Overcome with astonishment, the little dog stopped, hesitated a moment, then lay down on the ground, his eyes turned toward us, watching us disappear and whimpering with fright on the edge of the big city.

And a little later I was pleased, as you will understand, that I did not need to look at him any longer.

3

I have always thought that the human heart is a little like the ocean, subject to tides, that joy rises in it in a steady flow, singing of waves, good fortune, and bliss; but afterward, when the high sea withdraws, it leaves an utter desolation in our sight. So it was with me that day.

We had gone back across almost the whole enormous city —less enormous perhaps than scattered, strangely, widely spread out. The eagerness of the day diminished. I even think the sun was about to disappear. Our monster cart plunged, like some worn-out beast, toward the inconvenient, rambling neighborhoods that lay at the exact opposite end of the city to the one from which we had come.

Florence was whiling away the time by opening the drawers of an old chest and thrusting her hand into the muddle inside—the exact embodiment, it seemed to me, of this day—bits of faded ribbon; old postcards on whose backs someone had one day written: Splendid weather, Best love and kisses; a quill from a hat; electricity bills; gas reminders; a small child's shoe. The disagreeable little girl gathered up handfuls of these things, examined them, read, laughed. At one point, sensing my disapproval, she looked up, saw me watching her rummage, and thumbed her nose in spite.

The day declined further. Once more we were in sad little

streets, without trees, so much like the one from which we had taken the Smiths that it seemed to me we had made all this journey for nothing and were going to end up finally at the same shack from which I had hoped to remove them.

At the end of each of these little streets the infinite prairie once more appeared but now almost dark, barely tinted, on the rim of the horizon, with angry red—the pensive, melancholy prairie of my childhood.

At last we had arrived.

Against that red horizon a small lonely house stood out black, quite far from its neighbors—a small house without foundations, set upon the ground. It did not seem old but it was already full of the odor and, no doubt, the rags and tatters of the people who had left it a short time ago. However, they had not left a single light bulb in place.

In the semi-darkness Mrs. Smith began to search through her bundles, lamenting that she was sure she had tucked two or three carefully away but no longer remembered where. Her husband, who had arrived a short time before us, distressed by the dimness and the clumsiness of his wife, began to accuse her of carelessness. The children were hungry; they started to cry with fretful frightened voices, in an importunate tone that reminded me of the whimpering of the little dog. The parents distributed a few slaps, a little haphazardly, it seemed to me. Finally Mrs. Smith found a light bulb. A small glow shone forth timidly, as if ashamed at having to illuminate such a sad beginning.

One of the children, tortured by some strange preference, began to implore, "Let's go home. This isn't our home. Oh let's go back home!"

Mrs. Smith had come across a sack of flour, a frying pan and some eggs while she was searching for light bulbs and now she courageously set to work preparing a meal for her family. It was this, I think, that saddened me most: this poor woman, in the midst of complete disorder and almost in the dark, beginning to make pancakes. She offered some to me.

I ate a little, for I was very hungry. At that moment I believe she was sorry she had abandoned the little dog. This was the one small break in the terrible ending of this day.

Meanwhile Monsieur Pichette, in a grumbling anxiety to be finished, had completely emptied the cart. As soon as everything was dumped on the ground in front of the door, he came and said to Mr. Smith, "That's five dollars."

"But you have to help me carry it all in," said Mr. Smith.

"Not on your life. I've done all I have to."

Poor Mr. Smith fumbled in his pocket and took out five dollars in bills and small change, which he handed to the mover.

The latter counted the money in the weak glimmer that came from the house and said, "That's it. We're quits."

In this glimmer from the house I noticed that our poor horses were also very tired. They blinked their eyes with a lost expression, the result of too many house movings, no doubt. Perhaps horses would prefer to make the same trip over and over again—in this way they would not feel too estranged from their customary ways. But, always setting out on new routes, toward an unknown destination, they must feel disconcerted and dejected. I had time, by hurrying, to fetch them each a handful of tender grass at the end of the street where the prairie began.

What would we have had to say to each other on our way back? Nothing, certainly, and so we said nothing. Night had fallen, black, sad, and impenetrable, when we finally reached the old stable, which had once seemed to me to contain more magic and charm than even the cave of Aladdin.

The mover nevertheless reached out his hand to help me down from the cart. He was one of those people—at least I thought so then—who, after being surly and detestable all day, try at the last moment to make amends with a pleasant word for the bad impression they have created. But it was too late, much too late.

"You're not too tired?" he asked, I believe.

I shook my head and after a quick good night, an unwilling thank you, I fled. I ran toward my home, the sidewalk resounding in the silence under my steps.

I don't believe I thought of rejoicing at what I was returning to—a life that, modest as it was, was still a thousand miles away from that of the Pichettes and the Smiths. And I had not yet realized that this whole shabby, dull, and pitiless side of life that the move had revealed to me today would further increase my frenzy to escape.

I was thinking only of my mother's anxiety, of my longing to find her again and be pardoned by her—and perhaps pardon her in turn for some great mysterious wrong whose point I did not understand.

She was in such a state of nervous tension, as a matter of fact—although neighbors had told her I had gone off early with the Pichettes—that when she saw me it was her exasperation that got the upper hand. She even raised her hand to strike me. I did not think of avoiding punishment. I may even have wanted it. But at that moment a surge of disillusionment came over me—that terrible distress of the heart after it has been inflated like a balloon.

I looked at my mother and cried, "Oh why have you said a hundred times that from the seat of the covered wagon on the prairie in the old days the world seemed renewed, different, and so beautiful?"

She looked at me in astonishment.

"Ah, so that's it!" she said.

And at once, to my profound surprise, she drew me toward her and cradled me in her arms.

"You too then!" she said. "You too will have the family disease, departure sickness. What a calamity!"

Then, hiding my face against her breast, she began to croon me a sort of song, without melody and almost without words.

"Poor you," she intoned. "Ah, poor you! What is to become of you!"

Identities

 Normally, he goes clean shaven into the world but the promise of a Saturday liquid with sunshine draws him first from his study to the backyard, from there to his front lawn. The smell of burning leaves stirs the memories of childhood car rides, narrow lanes adrift with yellow leaves, girls on plodding horses, unattended stands piled high with pumpkins, onions, beets so that each one was, in its own way, a still life. Always, there were salmon tins glinting with silver, set above hand painted signs instructing purchasers to deposit twenty-five or fifty cents. This act of faith containing all the stories he has read in childhood about the North—cabins left unlocked, filled with supplies for hapless wayfarers—wakes in him a desire to temporarily abandon the twice-cut yards and hundred year old oaks.

He does not hurry for he has no destination. He meanders, instead, through the suburban labyrinth of cul-de-sacs, bays and circles, losing and finding himself endlessly. Becoming lost is made all the easier because the houses appear identical, repeat themselves with

W.D.
VALGARDSON

superficial variations. There grows within him, however, a vague unease with symmetry, with nothing left to chance, no ragged edges, no unkempt vacant lots, no houses rendered unique by necessity and indifference.

The houses have all faced toward the sun. They have had no artificial divisions. There is room enough for everyone. Now, as he passes grey stone gates, the yards are all proscribed by stiff picket fences and, quickly, a certain untidiness creeps in: a fragment of glass, a chocolate bar wrapper, a plastic horse, cracked sidewalks with ridges of stiff grass.

Although he has on blue jeans—matching pants and jacket made in Paris—he is driving a grey Mercedes Benz. Gangs of young men follow the car with unblinking eyes. The young men stand and lean in tired, watchful knots close to phone booths and seedy looking grocery stores.

Their hair glistens as though shellacked. Their leather jackets gleam with studs. Eagles, tigers, wolves, and serpents ride their backs.

He passes a ten foot wire fence enclosing a playground bare of equipment and pounded flat. The gate is double locked, the fence cut and rolled into a cone. Three boys throw stones at pigeons. Paper clogs the fence like drifted snow. The school is sheathed in heavy screens. Its yellow brick is pock-marked, chipped.

The houses are squat, as though they have been taller and have, slowly, sunk into the ground. Each has a band of dirt around the bottom. The blue glow of television sets light the windows. On the front steps of a red-roofed house, a man sits. He wears black pants, a tartan vest, a brown snap-brimmed hat. Beside him is a suitcase.

Fences here are little more than fragments. Cars jam the narrow streets and he worries that he might strike the unkempt children who dart back and forth like startled fish. Darkness has quietly been settling like soot. Street lights come on. He takes them as a signal to return the way he came but it has been a reckless, haphazard path. Retracing it is impossible. He is overtaken by sudden guilt. He has left no message for his wife.

There have been no trees or drifting leaves, no stands covered in produce, no salmon tins, but time has run away with him. His wife, he realizes, will have returned from bridge, his children gathered for supper. He also knows that, at first, they will have explained his absence on a neighbour's hospitality and gin. However, by the time he can return, annoyance will have blossomed into alarm. His safe return will, he knows from childhood and years of being locked in domestic grief, degenerate to recriminations and apology.

Faced with this, he decides to call the next time he sees a store or phone booth. So intent is he upon the future that he dangerously ignores the present and does not notice the police car, concealed in the shadows of a side street, nose out and follow him.

Ahead, there is a small store with windows covered in handpainted signs and vertical metal bars. On the edge of the light, three young men and a girl slouch. One of the men has a beard and, in spite of the advancing darkness, wears sunglasses. He has on a fringed leather vest. His companions wear leather jackets. Their peaked caps make their heads seem flat, their foreheads non-existent. The girl is better looking than she should be for such companions. She is long-legged and wears a white turtle-necked sweater that accentuates her breasts.

In spite of his car, he hopes his day old beard which he strokes upward with the heel of his hand, will, when combined with his clothes, provide immunity. He slips his wallet into his shirt pocket, does up the metal buttons on his jacket and slips a ten dollar bill into his back pocket. Recalling a television show, he decides that if he is accosted, he will say that the ten is all he's got, that he stole the car and ask them if they know a buyer.

He edges nervously along the fender and past the grille.

The store window illuminates the sidewalk like a stage. Beyond the light, everything is obscured by darkness. He is so intent upon the three men and the girl that he does not notice the police car drift against the curb, nor the officer who is advancing with a pistol in his hand.

When the officer, who is inexperienced, who is nervous because of the neighborhood, who is suspicious because of the car and, because he has been trained to see an unshaven man in blue jeans as a potential thief and not as a probable owner, orders him to halt, he is caught by surprise. When he turns part way around and recognizes the uniform, he does not feel fear but relief. Instinctively relaxing, certain of his safety, in the last voluntary movement of his life, he reaches his hand not upward in a gesture of submission but toward his wallet for his identity.

Antigone

My father ruled a kingdom on the right bank of the river. He ruled it with a firm hand and a stout heart though he was often more troubled than Moses, who was simply trying to bring a stubborn and moody people under God's yoke. My father ruled men who thought they were gods or the instruments of gods or, at very least, god-afflicted and god-pursued. He ruled Atlas who held up the sky, and Hermes who went on endless messages, and Helen who'd been hatched from an egg, and Pan the gardener, and Kallisto the bear, and too many others to mention by name. Yet my father had no thunderbolt, no trident, no helmet of darkness. His subjects were delivered bound into his hands. He merely watched over them as the hundred-handed ones watched over the dethroned Titans so that they wouldn't bother Hellas again.

Despite the care which my father took to maintain an atmosphere of sober common sense in his whole establishment, there were occasional outbursts of self-indulgence which he could not control. For instance, I have seen

SHEILA
WATSON

Helen walking naked down the narrow cement path under the chestnut trees for no better reason, I suppose, than that the day was hot and the white flowers themselves lay naked and expectant in the sunlight. And I have seen Atlas forget the sky while he sat eating the dirt which held him up. These were things which I was not supposed to see.

If my father had been as sensible through and through as he was thought to be, he would have packed me off to boarding school when I was old enough to be disciplined by men. Instead he kept me at home with my two cousins who, except for the accident of birth, might as well have been my sisters. Today I imagine people concerned with our welfare would take such an environment into account. At the time I speak of most people thought us fortunate—especially the girls whose fathers' affairs had come to an unhappy issue. I don't like to revive old scandal and I wouldn't except to deny it: but it takes only a few impertinent newcomers in any community to force open cupboards which had been decently sealed by time. However, my father was so busy setting his kingdom to rights that he let weeds grow up in his own garden.

As I said, if my father had had all his wits about him he would have sent me to boarding school—and Antigone and Ismene too. I might have fallen in love with the headmaster's daughter and Antigone might have learned that no human being can be right always. She might have found out besides that from the seeds of eternal justice grow madder flowers than any which Pan grew in the gardens of my father's kingdom.

Between the kingdom which my father ruled and the wilderness flows a river. It is this river which I am crossing now. Antigone is with me.

How often can we cross the same river, Antigone asks.

Her persistence annoys me. Besides, Heraklitos made nonsense of her question years ago. He saw a river too—the Inachos, the Kephissos, the Lethaios. The name doesn't matter. He said: See how quickly the water flows. However agile a man is, however nimbly he swims, or runs, or flies, the water slips away before him. See, even as he sets down his foot the water is displaced by the stream which crowds along in the shadow of its flight.

But after all, Antigone says, one must admit that it is the same kind of water. The oolichans run in it as they ran last year and the year before. The gulls cry above the same banks. Boats drift towards the Delta and circle back against the current to gather up the catch.

At any rate, I tell her, we're standing on a new bridge. We are standing so high that the smell of mud and river weeds passes under us out to the straits. The unbroken curve of the bridge protects the eye from details of river life. The bridge is foolproof as a clinic's passport to happiness.

The old bridge still spans the river, but the cat-walk with its cracks and knot-holes, with its gap between planking and handrail has been torn down. The centre arch still grinds open to let boats up and down the river, but a child can no longer be walked on it or swung out on it beyond the water-gauge at the very centre of the flood.

I've known men who scorned any kind of bridge, Antigone says. Men have walked into the water, she says, or, impatient, have jumped from the bridge into the river below.

But these, I say, didn't really want to cross the river. They went Persephone's way, cradled in the current's arms, down the long halls under the pink feet of the gulls, under the booms and tow-lines, under the soft bellies of the fish.

Antigone looks at me.

There's no coming back, she says, if one goes far enough.

I know she's going to speak of her own misery and I won't listen. Only a god has the right to say: Look what I suffer. Only a god should say: What more ought I to have done for you that I have not done?

Once in winter, she says, a man walked over the river.

Taking advantage of nature, I remind her, since the river had never frozen before.

Yet he escaped from the penitentiary, she says. He escaped from the guards walking round the walls or standing with their guns in the sentry-boxes at the four corners of the enclosure. He escaped.

Not without risk, I say. He had to test the strength of the ice himself. Yet safer perhaps than if he had crossed by the old bridge where he might have slipped through a knot-hole or tumbled out through the railing.

He did escape, she persists, and lived forever on the far side of the river in the Alaska tea and bulrushes. For where, she asks, can a man go farther than to the outermost edge of the world?

The habitable world, as I've said, is on the right bank of the river. Here is the market with its market stalls—the coops of hens, the longtongued geese, the haltered calf, the bearded goat, the shoving pigs, and the empty bodies of cows and sheep and rabbits hanging on iron hooks. My father's kingdom provides asylum in the suburbs. Near it are the convent, the churches, and the penitentiary. Above these on the hill the cemetery looks down and on the river itself.

It is a world spread flat, tipped up into the sky so that men and women bend forward, walking as men walk when they board a ship at high tide. This is the world I feel with my feet. It is the world I see with my eyes.

I remember standing once with Antigone and Ismene in the square just outside the gates of my father's kingdom. Here from a bust set high on a cairn the stone eyes of Simon Fraser look from his stone face over the river that he found.

It is the head that counts, Ismene said.

It's no better than an urn, Antigone said, one of the urns we see when we climb to the cemetery above.

And all I could think was that I didn't want an urn, only a flat green grave with a chain about it.

A chain won't keep out the dogs, Antigone said.

But his soul could swing on it, Ismene said, like a bird blown on a branch in the wind.

And I remember Antigone's saying: The cat drags its belly on the ground and the rat sharpens its tooth in the ivy.

I should have loved Ismene, but I didn't. It was Antigone I loved. I should have loved Ismene because, although she walked the flat world with us, she managed somehow to see it round.

The earth is an oblate spheroid, she'd say. And I knew that she saw it there before her comprehensible and whole like a tangerine spiked through and held in place while it rotated on the axis of one of Nurse's steel sock needles. The earth was a tangerine and she saw the skin peeled off and the world parcelled out into neat segments, each segment sweet and fragrant in its own skin.

It's the head that counts, she said.

In her own head she made diagrams to live by, cut and fashioned after the eternal patterns spied out by Plato as he rummaged about in the sewing basket of the gods.

I should have loved Ismene. She would live now in some prefabricated and perfect chrysolite by some paradigm which made love round and whole. She would simply live and leave destruction in the purgatorial ditches outside her own walled paradise.

Antigone is different. She sees the world flat as I do and feels it tip beneath her feet. She has walked in the market and seen the living animals penned and the dead hanging stiff on their hooks. Yet she defies what she sees with a defiance which is almost denial. Like Atlas she tries to keep the vaulted sky from crushing the flat earth. Like Hermes she brings a message that there is life if one can escape to it in the brush and bulrushes in some dim Hades beyond the river. It is defiance not belief and I tell her that this time we walk the bridge to a walled cave where we can deny death no longer.

Yet she asks her question still. And standing there I tell her that Heraklitos has made nonsense of her question. I should have loved Ismene for she would have taught me what Plato meant when he said in all earnest that the union of the soul with the body is in no way better than dissolution. I expect that she understood things which Antigone is too proud to see.

I turn away from her and flatten my elbows on the high wall of the bridge. I look back at my father's kingdom. I see the terraces rolling down from the redbrick buildings with their barred windows. I remember hands shaking the bars and hear fingers tearing up paper and stuffing it through the meshes. Diktynna, mother of nets and high leaping fear. O Artemis, mistress of wild beasts and wild men.

The inmates are beginning to come out on the screened verandas. They pace up and down in straight lines or stand silent like figures which appear at the same time each day from some depths inside a clock.

On the upper terrace Pan the gardener is shifting sprinklers with a hooked stick. His face is shadowed by the brim of his hat. He moves as economically as an animal between the beds of lobelia and geranium. It is high noon.

Antigone has cut out a piece of sod and has scooped out a grave. The body lies in a coffin in the shade of the magnolia tree. Antigone and I are standing. Ismene is sitting between two low angled branches of the monkey puzzle tree. Her lap is filled with daisies. She slits the stem of one daisy and pulls the stem of another through it. She is making a chain for her neck and a crown for her hair.

Antigone reaches for a branch of the magnolia. It is almost beyond her grip. The buds flame above her. She stands on a small fire of daisies which smoulder in the roots of the grass.

I see the magnolia buds. They brood above me, whiteness feathered on whiteness. I see Antigone's face turned to the light. I hear the living birds call to the sun. I speak private poetry to myself: Between four trumpeting angels at the four corners of the earth a bride stands before the altar in a gown as white as snow.

Yet I must have been speaking aloud because Antigone challenges me: You're mistaken. It's the winds the angels hold, the four winds of the earth. After the just are taken to paradise the winds will destroy the earth. It's a funeral, she says, not a wedding.

She looks towards the building.

Someone is coming down the path from the matron's house, she says.

I notice that she has pulled one of the magnolia blossoms from the branch. I take it from her. It is streaked with brown where her hands have bruised it. The sparrow which she has decided to bury lies on its back. Its feet are clenched tight against the feathers of its breast. I put the flower in the box with it.

Someone is coming down the path. She is wearing a blue cotton dress. Her cropped head is bent. She walks slowly carrying something in a napkin.

It's Kallisto the bear, I say. Let's hurry. What will my father say if he sees us talking to one of his patients?

If we live here with him, Antigone says, what can he expect? If he spends his life trying to tame people he can't complain if you behave as if they were tame. What would your father think, she says, if he saw us digging in the Institution lawn?

Pan comes closer. I glower at him. There's no use speaking to him. He's deaf and dumb.

Listen, I say to Antigone, my father's not unreasonable. Kallisto thinks she's a bear and he thinks he's a bear tamer, that's all. As for the lawn, I say quoting my father without conviction, a man must have order among his own if he is to keep order in the state.

Kallisto has come up to us. She is smiling and laughing to herself. She gives me her bundle.

Fish, she says.

I open the napkin.

Pink fish sandwiches, I say.

For the party, she says.

But it isn't a party, Antigone says. It's a funeral.

For the funeral breakfast, I say.

Ismene is twisting two chains of daisies into a rope. Pan has stopped pulling the sprinkler about. He is standing beside Ismene resting himself on his hooked stick. Kallisto squats down beside her. Ismene turns away, preoccupied, but she can't turn far because of Pan's legs.

Father said we never should
Play with madmen in the wood.

I look at Antigone.

It's my funeral, she says.

I go over to Ismene and gather up a handful of loose daisies from her lap. The sun reaches through the shadow of the magnolia tree.

It's my funeral, Antigone says. She moves possessively toward the body.

An ant is crawling into the bundle of sandwiches which I've put on the ground. A file of ants is marching on the sparrow's box.

I go over and drop daisies on the bird's stiff body. My voice speaks ritual words: Deliver me, O Lord, from everlasting death on this dreadful day. I tremble and am afraid.

The voice of a people comforts me. I look at Antigone. I look her in the eye.

It had better be a proper funeral then, I say.

Kallisto is crouched forward on her hands. Tears are running down her cheeks and she is licking them away with her tongue.

My voice rises again: I said in the midst of my days, I shall not see—

Antigone just stands there. She looks frightened, but her eyes defy me with their assertion.

It's my funeral, she says. It's my bird. I was the one who wanted to bury it.

She is looking for a reason. She will say something which sounds eternally right.

Things have to be buried, she says. They can't be left lying around anyhow for people to see.

Birds shouldn't die, I tell her. They have wings. Cats and rats haven't wings.

Stop crying, she says to Kallisto. It's only a bird.

It has a bride's flower in its hand, Kallisto says.

We shall rise again, I mutter, but we shall not all be changed.

Antigone does not seem to hear me.

Behold, I say in a voice she must hear, in a moment, in the twinkling of an eye, the trumpet shall sound.

Ismene turns to Kallisto and throws the daisy chain about her neck.

Shall a virgin forget her adorning or a bride the ornament of her breast?

Kallisto is lifting her arms towards the tree.

The bridegroom has come, she says, white as a fall of snow. He stands above me in a great ring of fire.

Antigone looks at me now.

Let's cover the bird up, she says. Your father will punish us all for making a disturbance.

He has on his garment, Kallisto says, and on his thigh is written King of Kings.

I look at the tree. If I could see with Kallisto's eyes I wouldn't be afraid of death, or punishment, or the penitentiary guards. I wouldn't be afraid of my father's belt or his honing strap or his bedroom slipper. I wouldn't be afraid of falling into the river through a knot-hole in the bridge.

But, as I look, I see the buds falling like burning lamps and I hear the sparrow twittering in its box: Woe, woe, woe because of the three trumpets which are yet to sound.

Kallisto is on her knees. She is growling like a bear. She lumbers over to the sandwiches and mauls them with her paw.

Ismene stands alone for Pan the gardener has gone.

Antigone is fitting a turf in place above the coffin. I go over and press the edge of the turf with my feet. Ismene has caught me by the hand.

Go away, Antigone says.

I see my father coming down the path. He has an attendant with him. In front of them walks Pan holding the sprinkler hook like a spear.

What are you doing here? my father asks.

Burying a bird, Antigone says.

Here? my father asks again.

Where else could I bury it? Antigone says.

My father looks at her.

This ground is public property, he says. No single person has any right to an inch of it.

I've taken six inches, Antigone says. Will you dig the bird up again?

Some of his subjects my father restrained since they were moved to throw themselves from high places or to tear one another to bits from jealousy or rage. Others who disturbed the public peace he taught to walk in the airing courts or to work in the kitchen or in the garden.

If men live at all, my father said, it is because discipline saves their life for them.

From Antigone he simply turned away.

Biographical and
Critical Notes on
Individual Authors

EDNA ALFORD

Edna Alford was born and spent the early years of her life in Turtleford, Saskatchewan. Later she moved to Saskatoon where she attended high school and began her writing career. While studying English at the University of Saskatchewan, she spent her summers working at various nursing homes, an experience that inspired many of the stories in her first anthology, the award-winning *A Sleep Full of Dreams*. Her present home is in Livelong, Saskatchewan where she lives with her husband and son. Alford gives readings in high schools, encouraging young writers whenever she can. She has taught at the Okanagan Summer School of the Arts and at Mount Royal College in Calgary. She is currently writer-in-residence at the Regina Public Library.

All of Alford's stories reflect her interest in the ways in which an individual's perceptions of the world affect his or her life. In her first collection of stories, she focuses on the differences between the world of the spirit and the world of the flesh. In her second collection, *The Garden of Eloise Loon*, she is particularly concerned with "our loss of long-distance vision".

ERNEST BUCKLER

Ernest Buckler was born in Dalhousie West, Annapolis County, Nova Scotia and, with the exception of five years in Toronto working with a life insurance company, he lived there on the family farm until his death in 1985. He was educated at Dalhousie University and at the University of Toronto. Buckler has won numerous prizes and medals for his writing, including the **Canada Centennial Medal** (1967) and the **Stephen Leacock Medal for Humour** (1977). He has honorary degrees from three Canadian universities. Best known for his first novel, *The Mountain and the Valley*, Buckler has also written several articles, a book of humorous sketches, a book of short stories and *Ox Bells and Fireflies*, reminiscences and anecdotes that reveal the author's passionate fondness for rural life in the Annapolis Valley.

Like *The Mountain and the Valley*, many of Buckler's stories are concerned with the relationship between father and son, a relationship which, although plagued with misunderstandings, is irradiated by mutual trust and affection. Buckler's love of language, his desire to make the reader see what he sees, and his use of lucid and memorable figurative language characterize all his work.

MATT COHEN

Born in Kingston, Ontario, Matt Cohen moved with his family to Ottawa where he received his early education. After obtaining both his B.A. and M.A. degrees from the University of Toronto, he taught the philosophy of religion for a year at McMaster University. He stopped teaching in 1968 to devote his full time to writing. In 1975 he was writer-in-residence at the University of Alberta and in 1981 he held the same post at the University of Western Ontario. Cohen spends most of his spare time on the land he owns north of Kingston, Ontario. Although Cohen has written reviews, radio and television plays, a book of poetry, and a children's book, he is best known for his novels and three volumes of short stories. Cohen's stories have been collected in *The Expatriot* (1982).

The motif of the divided self figures prominently in many of Cohen's works, as do images of separation and transition; one often feels that some major change is necessary before the protagonist can achieve any kind of wholeness. Although most of Cohen's novels are rooted firmly in realism, several of his stories and one of his early novels explore worlds that lie on one side or the other of the thin line that separates the real from the surreal.

MAVIS GALLANT

Mavis Gallant was born in Montreal and attended school both in Montreal and in the eastern United States. After working at the National Film Board for a short time and writing for the *Montreal Standard*, Gallant moved to Europe in her late twenties with hopes of obtaining from the international market the critical recognition that her own country had not given to her. She met with success shortly thereafter. Thirty years later Canada acknowledged her achievements and granted her the **Governor-General's Award** for her sixth collection of stories, *Home Truths* (1981). In 1981 she was also made an officer of the Order of Canada. In 1983 and 1984 Gallant accepted the post of writer-in-residence at the University of Toronto. In addition to her short-story collections, Gallant has published two novels and a play which was first performed at Toronto's Tarragon Theatre in 1982.

In many of Gallant's works the central conflict focuses on a clash between people from different cultures: the immigrant versus the native, the newcomer versus the established citizen, the uneducated versus the educated, and so on. But behind this surface conflict lies a theme that makes Gallant's stories, regardless of their settings, timeless and universal: the arrogant and self-complacent can rarely recognize the basic humanity of anyone whose circumstances differ from their own.

JACK HODGINS

Jack Hodgins was born and grew up in the Conox Valley area of Vancouver Island. He studied creative writing at the University of British Columbia under Earle Birney and graduated with his B.Ed. in 1961. He taught English at Nanaimo High School for several years, travelled to Ireland and Japan, then returned to Canada in the 1970s. After the publication of his first volume of short stories, *Spit Delaney's Island* in 1976, he became writer-in-residence at Simon Fraser University, moving on to the same post at the University of Ottawa two years later. In addition to editing several anthologies, Hodgins has published another volume of short stories and several novels including *The Resurrection of Joseph Bourne* which won the **Governor-General's Award** in 1979.

Hodgins's stories reveal that he is a master of many modes: comic, elegiac, allegorical, and ironic. He can sympathize with characters like Crystal who are submerged by their environment, yet show admiration for characters like Spit Delaney who go to any lengths to avoid being thus submerged.

HUGH HOOD

Born and educated in Toronto, Hugh Hood received his Ph.D. from the University of Toronto in 1955. In 1961 he joined the Department of English at the Université de Montréal and has taught there ever since. One of Canada's most prolific writers, Hood has published six collections of short stories, eight novels, a biography of Jean Beliveau, as well as a collection of personal and journalistic essays, *The Governor's Bridge Is Closed*. His series of twelve interrelated novels, *The New Age*, is expected to be completed by the year 2000.

Hood's attention to detail, and his ability to imbue these details with a significance that goes beyond mere verisimilitude, characterize almost everything he writes. Implicit in his work is his belief in the supremacy of the human soul. He also believes in the imagination's ability to see in wholes and to create from the chaos of the physical world a cosmos of the spirit.

MARGARET LAURENCE

Born in the prairie town of Neepawa, Manitoba, Margaret Laurence knew before she was a teenager that she wanted to be a writer. When she was only thirteen, she invented the name Manawaka for a fictional prairie town, a town that was later to be the setting for her four major novels. After graduating in Honours English from United College, Winnipeg, Laurence began to work as a reporter for the *Winnipeg Citizen*. In 1950 she moved with her husband to Somaliland, and later to Ghana, in Africa. Laurence's experiences in Africa form the basis for her first short-story collection, *The Tomorrow-Tamer* (1960). In 1962, Laurence and her children moved to England where they lived for ten years. In addition to her short stories, Laurence has published articles, reviews, a memoir, the semi-autobiographical *A Bird in the House*, four children's books, and four novels. In the 1970s she was writer-in-residence at several Ontario universities and in 1980 she became chancellor of Trent University. Laurence has received several awards for her writing, among them the **Governor-General's Award** for both *A Jest of God* (1966) and *The Diviners* (1974). Laurence presently resides in Lakefield, Ontario.

Laurence has said that when she is writing a book she lives not only with her own family but also with the characters she has created. Her concern is always to get inside her characters' dilemmas, to see them not from the point of view of an outsider but from the point of view of the characters themselves.

STEPHEN LEACOCK

Born in Swanmore, England, Stephen Leacock and his family moved to the Lake Simcoe area in Ontario when he was only seven. Leacock was educated at Upper Canada College and later at the University of Toronto and the University of Chicago. In 1903, after receiving his doctorate, he joined the Department of Economics and Political

Science at McGill University where he taught until his retirement in 1936. In 1909 he and his wife built a summer home on Lake Couchiching near Orillia, Ontario, where he spent most of his free time until his death in 1944. One of Canada's most prolific writers, Leacock has published more than fifty books, the most popular being *Literary Lapses* and *Sunshine Sketches of a Little Town*. Also popular are his volumes of nonsense novels. The **Stephen Leacock Medal for Humour** was instituted in 1947 and is awarded annually for the best book of humour, be it poetry, prose, or drama.

Leacock's humour ranges from the parodic, "Gertrude the Governess", to the gently satiric, "The Marine Excursion of the Knights of Pythias". In works such as *Sunshine Sketches of a Little Town*, much of the humour derives from the voice of Leacock's naive and gullible narrator.

ALICE MUNRO

Alice Munro grew up in Wingham, Ontario, a small town near Lake Huron. She studied at the University of Western Ontario before moving to Vancouver. She has three children and is presently living in Clinton, Ontario with her husband. Her first volume of short stories, *Dance of the Happy Shades*, won the **Governor-General's Award** for fiction in 1968. Three subsequent books of short stories have also won high critical acclaim, including *Who Do You Think You Are?* which won the **Governor-General's Award** in 1978. Munro's novel, *Lives of Girls and Women*, formed the basis of a CBC drama starring Munro's daughter, Jenny.

In most of Munro's stories, the action is perceived through the consciousness of a girl or woman, even though the protagonist may be male. So authentic is this narrative voice that readers often mistakenly assume that Munro's stories are autobiographical. While they are usually not autobiographical, her stories do reflect a world that the reader immediately recognizes as honest, familiar, and deeply human. Munro shows particular concern for the young, the poor, the old, the uneducated, the inarticulate—in short, for all those who need a spokesperson because they are unable to speak for themselves.

SINCLAIR ROSS

Sinclair Ross was born and grew up near Prince Albert, Saskatchewan. After finishing high school, he worked as a clerk in several
banks in his home province. Later he moved to Winnipeg and from
there to Montreal where he joined the Royal Bank. Except for a short
stint in the Canadian army in the 1940s, Ross remained with the
Royal Bank until his retirement in 1968. Following his retirement,
Ross spent several years in Greece and Spain and then returned to
Vancouver in 1980. Ross has published two volumes of short stories,
The Lamp at Noon and Other Stories (1968) and *The Race and
Other Stories* (1982). He has also written four novels, among them
the highly acclaimed *As For Me and My House* (1941).

Ross is one of the few authors who is able to get inside the
consciousness of a character of the opposite sex as convincingly as he
does a character of his own sex. Many of his works are set in the
prairies during the depression. So integrated are the worlds he
creates that both landscape and characters seem to be oppressed by
some unidentifiable force that is bent on their subjugation. Only
rarely do Ross's characters emerge unscathed from their experiences.

GABRIELLE ROY

Born and educated in Saint-Boniface, Manitoba, Gabrielle Roy taught
in the rural schools of that province for several years before travel-
ling to England and France where she began her writing career.
Returning to Canada shortly after the war, Roy published her first
novel, *Bonheur d'occasion*, in 1945. Although completely bilingual,
Roy chose to write in her native French. Her first novel, *The Tin
Flute*, was translated in 1947 and won the **Governor-General's
Award** for fiction. In total, Roy has more than ten publications to her
credit: stories, novels, children's books, and a collection of non-fiction
translated as *First Lights of Earth* (1982). Perhaps her best-known
collections of stories are *Street of Riches*, translated in 1967, and
Children of My Heart, translated in 1979, four years before the
author's death. Both of these volumes have won the **Governor-
General's Award**.

The simplicity and clarity of Roy's style, together with the sympathy she brings to her characters and their dilemmas, make her a favourite with both the critics and the public. Whether Roy's stories are set in Montreal, the prairies, or the Arctic, they have a universality that speaks to us all.

W.D. VALGARDSON

Born in Winnipeg, William Dempsey Valgardson grew up and received his early education in Gimli, Manitoba. He received his B.A. from United College, his B.Ed. from the University of Manitoba, and his Master of Fine Arts from the University of Iowa. From 1970 to 1974, Valgardson was chairperson of the Department of English at Cottey College in Nevada. In 1975, he returned to Canada and joined the Department of Creative Writing at the University of Victoria, later becoming its chairperson. In addition to writing and teaching, Valgardson enjoys rock climbing and painting. He has published a volume of poetry and three volumes of short stories many of which draw on his interest in the Icelandic communities near Gimli. Valgardson has also published a novel, *Gentle Sinners*, which won the **Books in Canada** First-Novel Award in 1980.

Valgardson's subtle, uncompromising style vividly reflects the subtle, uncompromising—and often hostile—universe through which his characters move. Perhaps his most memorable stories are those suspense-filled tales where fate manipulates the protagonist into a corner from which there is little chance of escape.

SHEILA WATSON

Born in New Westminster, B.C., Sheila Watson grew up in the environs of the Provincial Mental Hospital where her father was superintendent. After receiving her public-school education in a convent, Watson obtained both her B.A. and M.A. degrees from the University of British Columbia. For the next few years she taught at various schools in British Columbia, most notably at Dog Creek in the interior, an experience which prompted her to write her celebrated novel, *The Double Hook* (1959). After receiving her Ph.D. from the University of Toronto, Watson joined the faculty of the

University of Alberta (1961). She retired in 1975 and moved to Nanaimo, British Columbia.

In her stories, as well as in her novel, Watson pares language down to the bone, depending not on description or explication to define her world, but on biblical cadences and the subtle juxtaposition of memorable images. Many of her protagonists are Everyman figures, engaged in the universal struggle of the human spirit against authoritarianism and repression.

Policy Statement

Prentice-Hall Canada Inc., Educational Book Division, and the editor of *Windows and Mirrors* are committed to the publication of instructional materials that are as bias-free as possible. This anthology was evaluated for bias prior to publication.

The editor and publisher also recognize the importance of appropriate reading levels and have therefore made every effort to ensure the highest degree of readability in the student text. The content has been selected, organized, and written at a level suitable to the intended audience. Standard readability tests have been applied to ensure an appropriate reading level.

Research indicates, however, that readability is affected by much more than word or sentence length; factors such as presentation, format and design, none of which are considered in the usual readability tests, also greatly influence the ease with which students read a book. These and many additional features have been carefully prepared to ensure maximum student comprehension.

Acknowledgments

"Under the I" by Edna Alford: reprinted by permission of Oolichan Books.

"Penny in the Dust" by Ernest Buckler. Used by permission of The Canadian Publishers, McClelland and Stewart Limited, Toronto.

"Heyfitz" by Matt Cohen from *Night Flights*. Copyright © 1978 by Matt Cohen. Reprinted by permission of Doubleday & Company, Inc.

"Jorinda and Jorindel" by Mavis Gallant from *Home Truths* © 1956. Reprinted by permission of Macmillan of Canada, A Division of Canada Publishing Corporation.

"By the River" by Jack Hodgins from *Spit Delaney's Island* © 1976. Reprinted by permission of Macmillan of Canada, A Division of Canada Publishing Corporation.

"After the Sirens" by Hugh Hood: reprinted by permission of the author.

"The Voices of Adamo" by Margaret Laurence. Used by permission of The Canadian Publishers, McClelland and Stewart Limited, Toronto.

"Gertrude the Governess: or Simple Seventeen" by Stephen Leacock. Used by permission of The Canadian Publishers, McClelland and Stewart Limited, Toronto.

"Walker Brothers Cowboy" by Alice Munro from *Dance of the Happy Shades*. Copyright © 1968 by Alice Munro. Published in Canada by McGraw-Hill Ryerson. All rights reserved.

"One's A Heifer" by Sinclair Ross. Used by permission of The Canadian Publishers, McClelland and Stewart Limited, Toronto.

"The Move" by Gabrielle Roy. Used by permission of The Canadian Publishers, McClelland and Stewart Limited, Toronto.

"Identities" by W.D. Valgardson: reprinted by permission of the author.

"Antigone" by Sheila Watson: from *Five Stories*, Coach House Press, 1984. Used by permission of the author.